THE MAPPING OF
NEW JERSEY

THE MAPPING OF
NEW JERSEY

The Men and the Art

JOHN P. SNYDER, 1926-

RUTGERS UNIVERSITY PRESS
New Brunswick, New Jersey

Library of Congress Cataloging in Publication Data

Snyder, John Parr, 1926–
  The mapping of New Jersey; the men and the art.

  Bibliography: p.
  1. Cartography—New Jersey. 2. New Jersey—Maps.
I. Title.
GA439.S64   912'.749   73–3336
ISBN 0–8135–0780–4.

The author is grateful for permission to quote from *A Topographical Description of the
Dominions of the United States of America,* by T. Pownall, copyright © 1949 by the
University of Pittsburgh Press.

This book is dedicated
to the memory of
GEORGE H. COOK AND C. C. VERMEULE
of the
New Jersey Geological
Survey

Contents

Civilians—133; Maps of the Shores—133; Flat Maps for a Curved State: Projections—134; A Mercator Map on Its Side—135; New Jersey Receives a Grid System—135; A Map from Many Cones—138; Johann Lambert's Conic Map—139; To Make a Modern Survey—142; The Map-Making Industry—144; General Drafting Co.: Road Maps with Finesse—144; Hammond Inc.: Perspective on the World—148; Millions for Free: The Road Maps—151; Maps for the Armchair: Atlases—162; Maps of Counties—167; Maps of Towns—168; Miscellaneous Maps— 169; What to Look Out for in Modern Maps—171

Appendixes

Illustrations

Preface

There are numerous excellent books about maps, map makers, mapping, and map projections, but New Jersey is seldom mentioned more than fleetingly. One exception is Harold J. Barker, Jr.'s, sixty-four-page *Mapping Digest for New Jersey,* published by the state in 1965. As the then topographic engineer for the state, and a licensed land surveyor, Mr. Barker wrote chiefly to aid professional surveyors, but he begins the booklet with a concise history of Jersey mapping.

Second must be listed Agnes B. Grametbaur's 1,540-page, unpublished typescript "Annotated Bibliography and Index of Atlases and Maps of New Jersey, 1800 to 1949." If only it could be updated and published! It became invaluable as my research progressed; a portion has been condensed in the appendix of this book.

Howard C. Rice, Jr., edited the useful booklet *New Jersey Road Maps of the 18th Century,* which was issued at the time of New Jersey's Tercentenary, 1964. The Princeton University Library published this nearly full-size reproduction of four maps, some containing several sections.

A fourth exception is Robert M. Lunny's *Early Maps of North America.* This forty-eight-page booklet was published in 1961 to coincide with an exhibit of old maps at the New Jersey Historical Society. The exhibit was cosponsored with New Jersey-based C. S. Hammond & Co. (now Hammond Inc.), which was celebrating its sixtieth anniversary as a map maker. Mr. Lunny, the Society's director, happily (and logically) emphasized New Jersey in his attractive and informative booklet.

Inspired by these references and the maps themselves, I have tried to bring together information which would interest any cartophile, but especially the amateur map lover of New Jersey, in the development of the mapping of his own state. The attempted emphasis is on the enjoyment of maps, with occasional interspersion of technical aspects which seem helpful.

The subject of this book is logically related to the scope of my more documentary book about the development of New Jersey's state, county and municipal boundaries, to which the reader can refer for more detail when this book touches upon that subject. The research for that book led to a further evaluation of the accuracy and content of existing maps.

I am indebted to many people, libraries and organizations. Especially do I thank (in alphabetical order) for extensive guidance and/or constructive comments Harold Barker, Jr., formerly of the State Bureau of Geology and Topography; Peter J. Guthorn, surgeon, author, and map expert; George J. Miller, Registrar, Board of Proprietors of East New Jersey; Donald Sinclair, Curator of Special Collections, Rutgers University Library; and my wife Jeanne, all of whom spent so many hours reviewing the manuscript.

In addition, I appreciate the very helpful assistance of Clark Beck and the Rutgers University Library; Charles F. Cummings and the New Jersey Reference Division of the Newark Public Library; Wilson Duprey and the New-York Historical Society; Wayne T. Fish, Frederic Parker, and General Drafting Co., Inc.; William Kerr, Walter H. Kolakowski, and the New Jersey Historical Society Library; William H. Taylor, Surveyor General, Western Division of New Jersey; Kate Wilson and Hammond Inc.; the Joint Free Public Library of Morristown and Morris Township; and the Princeton University Library Map Room and Rare Book Division. For additional illustrations and courtesies, I thank the Geography and Map Division of the Library of Congress, The Historical Society of Pennsylvania, and the University of Pittsburgh Press.

I hope this book has caught the essence of these vast resources.

John P. Snyder

Madison, New Jersey
March 1973

THE MAPPING OF
NEW JERSEY

New Jersey in relief. The relief on the large flat Coastal Plain is exaggerated with respect to the hilly northwest on this copy of an 1896 map. *N.J. Bureau of Geology and Topography.*

2

Introduction

THE FACE OF NEW JERSEY

Lying between the Delaware River and the Atlantic Ocean, and between an 1,800-foot peak called High Point and a flat peninsula ending at Cape May is a "historical accident" called New Jersey. We can divide the state into "physiographic" regions with a series of almost parallel diagonal lines running from northeast to southwest. Starting from the northwest, there are the Kittatinny Mountain Range, the Kittatinny Valley, the Highlands, the Piedmont, and—below the Perth Amboy-Trenton line—the vast Coastal Plain.[1] New Jersey's population is largely clustered about two cities not in New Jersey—New York and Philadelphia—with another center at Trenton and a strip along the shore.

New Jersey can be described in many ways: It is small—the fifth smallest state in area; it is large—eighth largest in population; it is rich in historical associations—the third state to ratify the Federal Constitution; it is heterogeneous, with substantial minorities—racial, religious, and national; it is compact, with an average of more people per square mile than any other state; it has a variety of scenery ranging from mountains to plains, from cozy lakes to open seashores.

New Jersey is famous for great inventions, truck gardening, industries, recreation, political corruption, organized crime, model courts, and progressive legislation. It was one of the last northern states to give up slavery, and one of the first to enforce equal opportunities, regardless of race, in employment and housing. It is a state of beauty and of ugliness, of immense problems and of great achievements.

Its problems, sometimes overwhelming, can almost fade into the background for a while if we take the full-scale New Jersey which

3

surrounds us and reduce it to the size of a sheet of paper. New Jersey then seems to become manageable: easily traced roads, rivers and boundaries, easily visited towns, lakes, and shores. With a little imagination, especially with topographic maps, we can see all of New Jersey without leaving home. The maps themselves, of course, were developed and improved only after the most strenuous work—traversing and surveying the hills and valleys of the region.

Speaking of topographic maps, New Jersey's were the first in the nation, but two hundred years earlier the face of New Jersey was barely recognizable on a map. It is to tell the story of transition from the crude beginnings to our modern precision maps that this book was written.

CHAPTER ONE

A Colony Takes Shape: Mapping Before 1750

DUTCH LANDINGS

It may be surprising that Holland was not only the homeland of the first European settlers of the future New Jersey; it was also the source of the first useful maps of the area. The fact is partly coincidental, since the Low Countries' period of western colonial expansion occurred at about the same time as their near-supremacy in map making—during the century from 1570 to 1670.[1]

The beauty of the Dutch maps was no small factor in the admiration given them by the contemporary world as well as by history. Reinforcing the beauty was a then-unequaled technical skill in assembling the results of explorations, in developing new map projections, and in mastering techniques of printing. Cartographers such as Gerardus Mercator, Abraham Ortelius, Henry Hondius, Willem Blaeu, and Jan Jansson produced superior results in the small country and in a short span of time. Their work continues to fascinate map enthusiasts, whether using maps as decorations or as source material.

The Dutch intrusion upon the lands of the Lenni-Lenape Indians began with exploration by Henry Hudson's crew in 1609 near Sandy Hook. The Dutch West India Company established the province of New Netherland in 1623. It consisted of all the present New Jersey area and the Hudson River valley, with rather unclear boundaries. Cornelius Mey (or May) led a ship of Dutch settlers up Godyns Bay (later called Delaware Bay) into Suydt Rivier, or South River—now the Delaware River. Their settlement in 1623 at Fort Nassau on

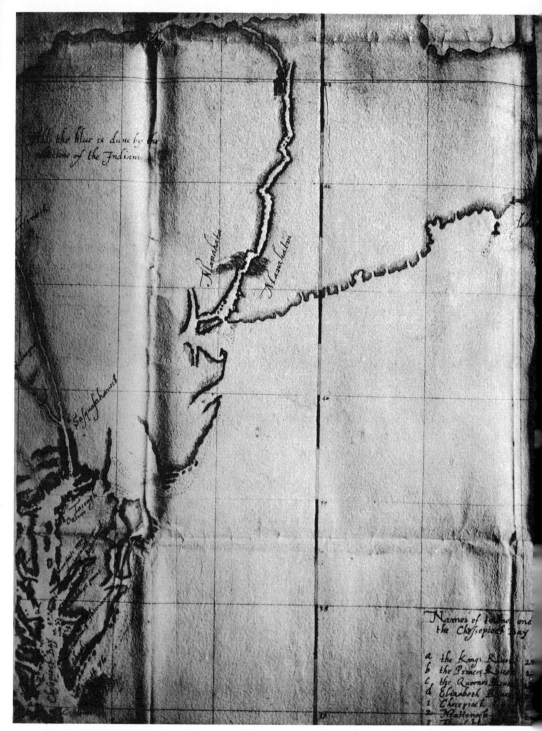

All the blue is done by the [*relations?*] of the Indians

Manahata

Manahata

Sasquesahanough

Iroquois

Chesapeack Bay

Names of [*places?*] one the Chessapioch Bay

a the Kings [*River?*]
b the Princes [*River?*]
c the Quornes [*River?*]
d Elizabeth [*River?*]
1 Chessapiock
2 Mattanock

Detail of the first map to give shape to the New Jersey area. An anonymous manuscript map, it is believed to have resulted from the English King's commission of 1610, following the return of Henry Hudson's crew from exploration of Sandy Hook and the Hudson River. From Stokes: *Iconography. Rutgers University Library.*

6

Timmer Kil (Timber Creek) met an unknown fate. All those left behind had disappeared before the Dutch returned in 1631.

Other attempts at Dutch settlement were only little more successful until 1630, when Michiel Pauw acquired Pavonia (named for him) in the area which is now Jersey City. Settlers soon arrived, but some of the Dutch refused to accept Indians as their neighbors. Reprisals and counterreprisals ended in destruction of all the Dutch settlements in Pavonia until Peter Stuyvesant repurchased the area —enlarged—from the Indians in 1659. A stockaded town called Bergen, 800 feet square, was established in 1660 at what is now Bergen Square in Jersey City. New Jersey now had its first permanent settlement.

Meanwhile Swedes and Finns had settled "New Sweden" on both sides of Delaware Bay and the lower Delaware River. They received so little support from Sweden, however, that they lasted as a Swedish colony only until 1655, when Stuyvesant sailed into the bay and conquered the territory.

Holland itself could maintain control of New Netherland for only nine more years. Settlers were so unconcerned and arms so limited that when England decided to lay claim to the area in 1664, Stuyvesant surrendered without firing a shot.

THE MAPPING OF NEW NETHERLAND

The New Jersey coastal area remained almost unknown to maps until the early 1600's. The Americas themselves were not shown on maps until Christopher Columbus's navigator Juan de la Cosa drew on oxhide a likeness of the eastern coast in 1500, but the New Jersey area was not identifiable. By then it was only vaguely known to Europeans—and to La Cosa—as a result of John Cabot's voyage in its vicinity for Henry VII of England in 1498. La Cosa's wavy coastline of the American mainland at the latitude of France bore five English banners and the inscription *mar descubierta por yngleses*—"sea discovered by the English." [2] Cabot's "discoveries" provided England with a presumptive basis for its future claims to the territory.

The name "America"—after explorer Amerigo Vespucci—was first proposed by German scholar and geographer Martin Waldseemüller in 1507. His globe of that year is lost, but the name is clearly shown on the South American continent of his 36-square-foot flat world map of the same year. His North America is severely truncated, unnamed, and unrecognizable except by its location.[3] Intensive exploration, however, gradually dispelled the ignorance of the coast.

As Italian, German, and French map makers leaped into the challenging venture of producing maps of the New World, the shape of North America became increasingly recognizable. It received a name when Gerardus Mercator applied the term *AMERICAE ps. sep.* ("north part of America") on his heart-shaped world map of 1538. By 1529, Florida and the Caribbean were easily recognized on maps. Nova Scotia and the Gulf of St. Lawrence were clearly indicated by 1544.[4]

One has to look at a map prepared as late as 1610, however, to see a line similar enough to the New Jersey coast to indicate that someone had actually inspected the region. That was the year in which King James I of England commissioned a map (based on Hudson's work) of which the only now-known copy reached the King of Spain and eventually the Spanish Archives. The map began to detail the coast with shapes resembling Staten Island, Sandy Hook, and Cape May. Manhattan and Long Island were still shown as part of the mainland.[5] Four years later, a map by explorer Adriaen Block showed improved detail north of Sandy Hook, but was useless south of there.[6] That map was not printed until 1635.

It remained for a cartographer named Johannes de Laet to issue, in 1630, the first detailed map focusing on the New England-Virginia coast. Entitled *Nova Anglia, Novum Belgium et Virginia* (Latin—standard for most early maps—for "New England, New Netherland and Virginia"), it identified "C. May," "Eyerhaven" (Egg Harbor), and the "Zuyd Rivier."[7] A neat but simple production, it was soon overshadowed by the beautiful *Nova Belgica et Anglia Nova* by Willem Janszoon Blaeu in 1635.

Extending from Penobscot Bay to Chesapeake Bay, Blaeu's map includes the future Jersey area, clearly showing the configuration of Sandy Hook, Little Egg Harbor, Delaware Bay, and islands which resemble Long Beach Island and Island Beach (which was an island as recently as 1810).

The map, oriented toward the west—as are several early maps of the east coast—is beautifully decorated with Indian canoes, elk, bears,

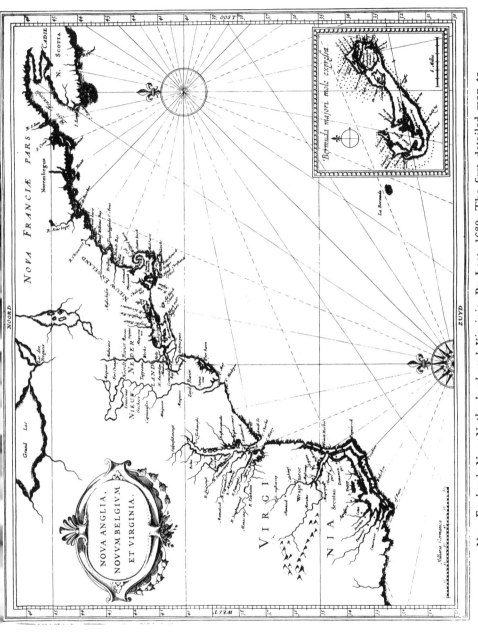

New England, New Netherland and Virginia. By Laet, 1630. The first detailed map to focus on the coast surrounding the future New Jersey. From Stokes: *Iconography. Rutgers University Library.*

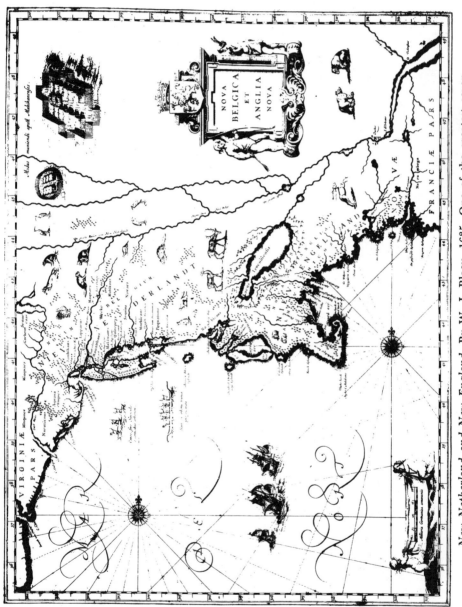

New Netherland and New England. By W. J. Blaeu, 1635. One of the greatest seventeenth century Dutch map makers enlivened the eastern seaboard with animals, canoes and other scenes which were to dominate many later maps of the area. From *Stokes: Iconography. Rutgers University Library.*

10

beavers and a bird's-eye view of Mohican Indian fortifications. It was a prototype for numerous later maps of the area by Visscher, Ottens, Seutter and others, often copied with geographical updating, but repeating some of the artistic embellishments complete to the animals' poses.

W. J. Blaeu was born in Alkmaar, Holland in 1571 and died in 1638 in Amsterdam. Studying for two years under the great Danish astronomer Tycho Brahe, he returned to Amsterdam to establish his shop. In 1599, Blaeu began to publish terrestrial and celestial globes, sea atlases, world atlases, and maps of towns. He signed his maps Guilielmus Janssonius or Willems Jan Zoon until 1617 and then switched to Guilielmus or G. Blaeu, to avoid confusion with rival cartographer Joannes Janssonius (or Jan Jansson). [8] His maps of the four continents—Europe, Asia, Africa and America—are among the most beautiful early maps produced by anyone, and are popular in many present-day antique map collections.

Blaeu was both perpetrator and victim of the all-too-popular map makers' habit of plagiarism, but there was no doubt about his outstanding abilities. The Blaeu family, father and sons, probably made the greatest contributions of the triumphant period of sixteenth- and seventeenth-century Dutch cartography.

TRACING THE COASTLINE

Known not for general map making, but as the possible (although far from certain) author of the first extensive coastal study of the Manhattan and Delaware Bay areas, was the cartographer of the Dutch West India Company, Joannes Vingboons. In 1639 the areas were surveyed, but the original maps are lost. Copies were made about thirty years later [9] and labeled *Manatus gelegen op de Noo[r]t Rivier* and *Caerte van de Suydt Rivier in Niew-Nederland.*

The first shows the locations and owners of about fifty plantations and bouweries in and near Manhattan. (A Dutch farmer lived in a bouwerie, but was the absentee owner of a plantation.) [10] The second map marks Indian tribes on the lower Suydt (South or Delaware) River. *Sant Punt* is now Sandy Hook. *Staten Eylant, Eyland Manatus, Cabo May, Remkokes Cil,* and *Timmer Kil* are labels which

Manhattan, copy of manuscript map attributed to J. Vingboons, 1639. The first extensive coastal survey of the future New York City area. *Geography and Map Division, Library of Congress.*

South River, copy of manuscript map attributed to J. Vingboons, 1639. Detailed coastal survey of southern New Jersey. *Geography and Map Division, Library of Congress.*

have survived to the present with little more than anglicization. The names *Noort Rivier* (Hudson River) and *Godyns Bay* (Delaware Bay) have not survived, except that the lower Hudson is still called the North River on shipboard.

NICOLAS VISSCHER SHOWS AN ELUSIVE BRANCH AT 41° 40'

Regardless of the priority that can largely be granted to Blaeu for meaningful maps of early colonial America, the accepted classic is Nicolas Joan ("Claes") Visscher's 1656 map. Published in numerous atlases of the period, it is entitled *Novi Belgii Novaeque Angliae nec non partis Virginiae tabula.* Although directly or indirectly inspired by Blaeu, Visscher incorporated much more information. His coastlines and inland rivers and lakes are well advanced beyond Blaeu's. The orientation is also to the north, rather than the west.

Visscher, a prominent figure in another outstanding Dutch cartographic family, produced a map of special interest for two reasons: (1) it shows a visitor's view of *Nieuw Amsterdam,* and (2) it was probably, according to boundary commissioners in 1769,[11] the map used by the English Duke of York (later King James II) in granting New Jersey to his court friends Sir George Carteret and John, Lord Berkeley, in 1664.

The second point has added significance when it is realized that over a century of boundary controversy between New Jersey and New York resulted from an erroneous conclusion the Duke reached from using the map. The Duke declared that New Jersey was to have "upon the West Delaware Bay or River," extending "to the Northward as far as the Northermost Branch of the said Bay or River of DelaWare, which is in ffourty one degrees and ffourty minutes of Latitude."[12] The northern boundary was to extend in a straight line from this point to 41° N. Lat. on the Hudson. Visscher's map shows a branch of the Delaware at 41° 40', its mouth near a settlement called Mecharienkonck, but there actually is no branch at or even near the latitude.

New Jersey preferred to abide by the latitude. New York agreed to it only until settlement began to increase in the area just south of

"Station Point," as the intersection of the latitude with the river was eventually called. It was then that New York moved to the self-serving conclusion that, while the Duke of York allegedly meant "the Head of Delaware Bay; which we assert to be at Reedy Island" (near Salem), New York would compromise by proposing as the terminus the "Forks of Delaware," where the Lehigh River empties into the Delaware at Easton.[13] This would have placed all of Sussex County and a substantial part of modern-day Warren, Morris, and Passaic Counties into the state of New York.

By the mideighteenth century, several other boundary lines had also been proposed. At the request of both provinces, the King appointed commissioners to establish the line. In 1769 they declared that the northern boundary line was meant to begin on the Delaware River at the mouth of the Mahackamack (probably a variation of Mecharienkonck) River, now the Neversink, and would run straight to the intersection of 41° north latitude with the Hudson River.[14] (The latter point was clearly described by the Duke, but the varying accuracy of surveys led to several locations during the early years.) There the northern boundary stands, except for deviations up to a half mile from a straight line. An abundance of magnetic iron ore in the Highlands unfortunately misled the surveyors when they ran their compass course in 1774.

Thus Visscher's map played a somewhat beclouded role in the origin of New Jersey. Someone has determined that its errors in the Jersey area range up to twenty-one miles in location.[15] Nevertheless, the map holds a wealth of names of Indian tribes, islands, rivers, and regions. It shows a large *lacus* or lake in future Jersey on a river which was probably meant to be the Musconetcong. Since this river is shown directly connected from the South (Delaware) River to the Hudson, Jersey is actually shown as an island.

The map was updated about 1690 by Visscher's grandson Nicolaus with no perceivable changes in topography. Pennsylvania was now named, as was *Nieu Iarsey*. The earlier *Nova Belgica sive* [or] *Nieuw Nederlandt* regional name remained, but added to it was *nu Niew Jorck* in grudging recognition of the permanent obsolescence of the former name after a brief restoration of the area to Holland for six months in 1673–74.[16] (This map is erroneously captioned as the 1656 map in the author's previous book.) [17]

In his classic *Iconography of Manhattan Island,* Stokes included a

New Netherland and New England. By Nicolas J. Visscher, 1656. Believed to have been the map used by the Duke of York in describing New Jersey in his grant

16

4. A nonexistent branch of the Delaware River shown at 41° 40′ North Lati-
e led to a century of boundary controversies between New Jersey and New
k. *New Jersey Historical Society.*

17

presumed prototype of unknown authorship, but published by Jan Jansson. Although it shows the area as of 1647–51, it may or may not have been actually issued after Visscher's. The Jansson map is generally almost identical to Visscher's, but especially lacks the view of New Amsterdam. Its cartouche and some of the drawings of animals are also distinctive.[18]

Of the many copies of Visscher's map by others, Adriaen vander Donck of Amsterdam prepared one of the earliest. Showing only the central portion of the map—from the *Zuydt* (Delaware) to the *Versche* (Connecticut) Rivers—Donck did little more than copy, placing words so they fell within the map, and relocating Visscher's view of New Amsterdam. His first edition named and placed Fort Christina (on the lower *Zuydt Rivier*) twice, although a later edition corrected this and added a missing scale of distances. The map lacks a cartouche or formal title, and can really be said to provide only a closer focus on the future New Jersey area. Dated 1656, it appeared in his book of that year describing New Netherland.

Visscher's map was almost completely copied without credit to him or anyone else by many map makers. Joost Danckers made almost no changes.[19] Arnoldus Montanus, about 1671, added his own cartouche, and spelled Jersey "Niev-Jarsey." [20] Hugo Allard of Amsterdam added a completely new cartouche, drastically revised the view of New Amsterdam, and added some more animals. He labeled the map *Totius Neo Belgii Nova et Accuratissima Tabula*, but left most other wording intact as to spelling, size and location. The map does include the name "Nieu Jarsey." It is also labeled *Restitutio,* since it was issued in honor of the temporary return of New York and New Jersey to the Dutch in 1673. Later copies of this version, complete with the same cartouche and the term *Restitutio* came forth, finally from Reinier and Iosua Ottens of Amsterdam as late as 1740.[21]

The German Matthew Seutter used Allard's view of New Amsterdam and generally copied the Visscher topography, but is distinctive in his cartouche. He added still more animals and many more descriptive labels. His Delaware River is markedly changed to an almost straight line north from the bend at the future site of Trenton. "Nieu Jarsey" becomes the German *Neu Iarsey,* south of *Neu Jorck.* Seutter's map also appeared about 1730 or 1740.

THE BLOODLESS CONQUEST BY ENGLAND

Although the English claimed the eastern seaboard because Cabot sailed along the coast in 1498, they made no attempt to interfere with the Dutch and Swedish settlements of the early 1600's. The Virginia charters of 1606, 1609, and 1612 included the New Jersey area in its entirety, but even those charters prohibited the London and Plymouth Companies from settling within one hundred miles of each other in the future Jersey area, where their grants over-lapped. Aside from serving as the site for some abortive attempts at English settlement near present-day Salem, New Jersey remained a disagreeable area for the English, Swedish, and Dutch until the establishment of Bergen in 1660.

In early 1664, however, King Charles II of England decided that the time had come to assert English domination over the area surrounding New Amsterdam. Economic competition with the Dutch, John Cabot's explorations, and the King's debts to friends and family combined to focus the operations on the middle Atlantic coast. In March Charles made a large grant to the Duke of York embracing much of Maine and the area between the Connecticut and Delaware Rivers as far north as the upper end of the Hudson River.

In May the Duke sent Colonel Richard Nicolls to claim the area. He had almost no difficulty accomplishing this feat, since Stuyvesant and his men surrendered without resistance. On August 29, 1664, New Netherland became an English possession.

Without the knowledge of Nicolls, the Duke of York had granted New Jersey to his friends Berkeley and Carteret on June 23 of the same year, presumably using the Visscher map to determine his boundaries. The limits were the Hudson River, the "main Sea," the Delaware Bay and River, and the controversial line from the Delaware River at 41° 40′ north latitude and/or a branch of the river, to 41° on the Hudson.

The northern boundary controversy described earlier was the most famous involving Jersey's limits, but almost all the other portions have been subjected to commissions or court decisions. For many years New Jersey was convinced that the Duke meant for her to have Staten Island, since the Hudson River could be interpreted as bounding either side of it, and the island is certainly closer to

Jersey than to the rest of New York. The boundary in the Delaware River was in the courts as recently as 1956.

The boundary through Delaware Bay would probably have followed the center, or the main ship channel, if it were not for the fact that the Duke of York, in his 1682 deed to William Penn, had included all the territory within a twelve-mile circle of New Castle, Delaware. Penn's "Three Lower Counties" of Pennsylvania became the State of Delaware, which held fast to the deed—at least to the Jersey side of Delaware Bay. New Jersey disagreed, with an eye on the oyster beds in the bay, and took the matter to court. In 1934, the U.S. Supreme Court finally resolved this dispute by placing the boundary, as Delaware claimed, along the Jersey low-water line within the twelve-mile radius, and along the middle of the ship channel above and below it.

The boundary on the ocean side is still not completely resolved. It is currently three "geographical" miles (6,087 feet each) from the low-water coastline, according to a 1953 federal law. This is a problem of international law, however, and New Jersey must follow the code applying to other coastal states.

The Duke of York originated the name New Jersey in his 1664 charter, honoring Carteret's defense of the Island of Jersey in the English Channel. The name Jersey is derived from Caesar. It has been conjectured that the Duke was further prompted to select this name because Visscher's map shows the New Jersey area as an island.[22]

With the establishment of New Jersey, English, Scottish, and Dutch settlement accelerated. Large tracts were purchased at Eliza-beth-Town, Middletown and Shrewsbury, Woodbridge, Piscataway, and Newark, in that order. With Bergen already in existence, there were seven towns or townships by 1667, all of them in northeast Jersey.

JOHN SELLER DRAWS A MAP OF JERSEY ALONE

At last New Jersey was a separate colony—born of friendships between duke and courtiers and nurtured by settlers who left not only England and Europe's mainland, but, in a number of cases,

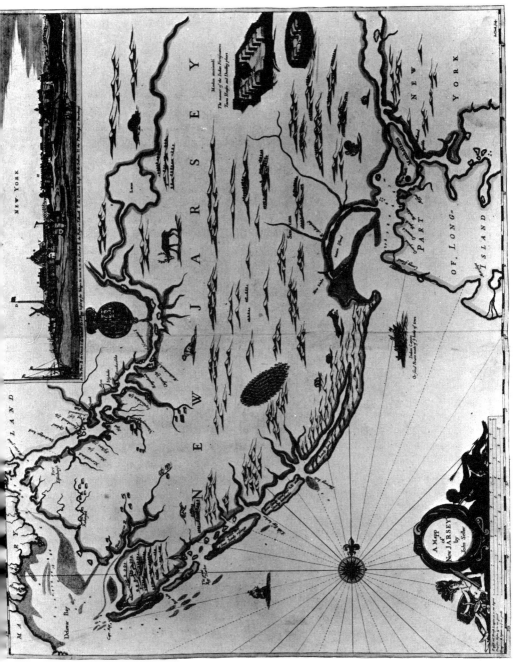

A Mapp of New Jarsey. By John Seller, 1675. The first map of the colony alone, and one of the first maps to use the terms New Jersey and New York. The Carteret coat of arms is shown. *New Jersey Historical Society.*

Connecticut, Long Island, and the future Maine. It could now expect maps confined to its own area.

The second map to use the term "New Jarsey," but apparently the first to show only that colony, was published by John Seller, the prolific hydrographer to Kings Charles II and James II, in his *Atlas Maritimus* of 1675. The copper engraving shows the colony as of 1664, and its first edition may have been separately published that year.[23] The second edition appeared about 1665, with the addition of the Carteret coat-of-arms and changes of some outlines.[24]

The shape of Seller's New Jersey is similar to the rather poor likeness shown on Visscher's map, but there are differences. His outline of south Jersey was almost certainly copied from "New Jarsy Pars" on a 1673 map of *Virginia and Maryland* by Maryland colonist Augustin Herrman, "the Bohemian." [25] Seller's maps of New Jersey are oriented toward the west. Inlets at Barnegat, Little Egg Harbor, Great Egg Harbor, "Bear Hole," and Cape May are shown, spaced with long pudgy islands marked with descriptions such as "Some wood land and some Sandy riseings."

The large *Lacus* of Visscher's map becomes very prominent on Seller's map. Perhaps it was meant to be the "Great Pond"—the forerunner of the artificially raised Lake Hopatcong. It may also have been an interpretation of the marshy "Drowned Lands" along the Wallkill River, noted on maps a hundred years later and not drained until 1826, but this is doubtful.[26] Visscher's view of Manhattan was copied by Seller as an inset with minor changes, and "The manner of the Indian Fortifications, Town Houses and Dwelling places" was pictorially copied with English wording instead of the Latin of Visscher.

Herrman's map also probably inspired a map of West Jersey and southeast Pennsylvania included with a 1698 promotional tract by Gabriel Thomas. The map gives little information beyond the Delaware River and Bay area.[27]

GEORGE KEITH DIVIDES ONE COLONY INTO TWO

New Jersey as a single colony was not to last long. Financial difficulties led Berkeley to sell his share of New Jersey to Quaker John

Fenwick in 1674. This was also the year in which New Jersey was returned to the English following the brief recapture by the Dutch. To reconfirm the charters of 1664, the King and the Duke were obliged to issue new grants. The Duke, distressed by Berkeley's sale of his half, only confirmed the grant to Carteret, giving him the northern and central part of the New Jersey tract. The southern part was ignored.

Fenwick, in turn, fell into debt and sold most of his purchase to four other Quakers, including William Penn. Penn and his associates, confident that they owned south Jersey in spite of the Duke's limited grant of 1674, wished to clear the title and also to control the Delaware River. Therefore, the four Quakers and Carteret concluded a "Quintipartite" deed in 1676 which divided New Jersey into two provinces: East and West New Jersey. Whether or not the Duke was in a position to challenge the legality of the deed, the agreement held, and strongly influenced the future of New Jersey. Actually the Duke of York confirmed the grant of West Jersey in 1680.

The division line was to proceed from Little Egg Harbor straight to the Duke's controversial point at 41° 40′ north latitude on the Delaware River. Although this line was not surveyed until 1743, its location was plotted by various map makers from its inception in 1676. Seller's map was revised in 1677 with the assistance of William Fisher to show the division line incorrectly running straight north from Little Egg Harbor. In addition, Seller and Fisher improved the coastlines of New York Bay and vicinity, and updated the bird's-eye view of New York by borrowing most of Hugo Allard's portrayal of a much more populous town. The title was lengthened from *A Mapp of New Jarsey* to *A Mapp of New Jersey in America.*

At this time, the two provinces of New Jersey entered into a period of control by multiple proprietors, with power of government existing until 1702, and with property ownership rights which still exist. After George Carteret died in 1680, his rights to East Jersey were bought by twelve men, nearly all Quakers, headed by William Penn. Each added a partner in 1683, increasing the number of East Jersey proprietors to twenty-four, of whom twenty were Quakers. Although several of them were English or Irish, the Scottish proprietors took the initiative in leadership and colonization. Governors, surveyors general, and other officers were appointed by the group. Certain resident proprietors were formed into a Board of

Proprietors of East Jersey in 1685, dealing chiefly with problems of land ownership and boundaries. This board continues to function, maintaining its office in Perth Amboy.

The West Jersey Proprietorship developed somewhat differently, with the power of government resting in single individuals at first rather than in the one hundred proprietors who owned the land in 1680. This power was spread to organizations such as the West Jersey Society in 1692, although the administration of land ownership had been transferred to a special group of proprietors in 1688. This latter group, called the Council of Proprietors of West New Jersey, has continued to operate from Burlington.

As the need for improved land surveying increased, John Reid, a Scottish settler of Amboy, prepared a number of local maps, such as a 1685 *Map of Plantations* . . . along the Raritan River, and a *Mapp of Rariton River,* both at a scale of 100 chains or 1¼ miles/ inch. The property outlines show extensive actual or incipient settlement. The latter map is the earliest known map to be engraved on copper within the present United States.[28]

At about the same time, although the map is undated, Reid prepared one of the earliest town maps in New Jersey. Drawn at only 8 chains (1/10 mile)/inch, *A Mapp of Perth Amboy in East New Jarsey/ Containing 1100 Acre Substract 30 for Waste Ground/ Remaines 1070 Acres* defines all the private tracts, from dozens of small lots at the mouth of the Raritan to the large plats inland. The colored manuscript original is held by the East Jersey Proprietors,[29] but an early print of a Simson engraving of this map was found among the Stevens papers acquired recently by the New Jersey Historical Society. (The Stevens family initiated and owned the state's first railroad.)

In 1687, the division line between East and West Jersey was finally surveyed, but not according to the line decreed in the deed of 1676. John Reid and William Emley, as Commissioners from East and West Jersey, respectively, chose a course from Little Egg Harbor, but running west of the prescribed path.

The surveyor general of East Jersey, George Keith, was hired to make the survey. This he did in the spring of 1687 north from Little Egg Harbor to the South Branch of the Raritan River, near the present location of Three Bridges. At the South Branch he stopped for reasons which are not clear. Within a few months, Governor

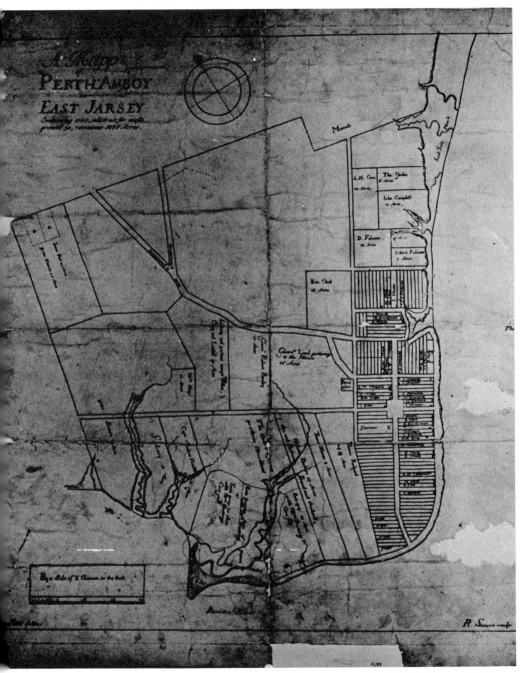

A Mapp of Perth Amboy in East Jarsey. An engraving of a map by John Reid, ca. 1685. One of the earlier town maps in New Jersey, this map shows the variety of lot sizes held by earlier settlers. *New Jersey Historical Society.*

Daniel Coxe of West Jersey was lamenting the inequitability of the line. Dr. Coxe, a London physician, had never set foot in America, but he owned a million acres in West Jersey. A year later, he and the governor of East Jersey, a devout Quaker philosopher named Robert Barclay—who also never saw America—agreed upon a revised boundary which included the Keith line only as far as it was already surveyed. From the South Branch of the Raritan, the new line progressed eastward via the North Branch, and the Passaic and the Pequannock Rivers to the New York line.

This Keith-Coxe-Barclay line—and not the Quintipartite deed line—became the basis for county boundaries which in many portions continue to the present. The Quintipartite deed line, finally surveyed in 1743 by John Lawrence, affects deeds to private property. The confusion about the lines is understandable—and persistent.

George Keith (1639?–1716) was an outstanding lay leader of the Religious Society of Friends, or Quakers. The philosophy of the Society led to many congregations without hired clergymen. (This is still true in New Jersey and many other Eastern areas.) Friends relied on the "Inner Light" to inspire and speak through its members and attenders not only during the week, but also during the "unprogrammed" Meetings for Worship. A close friend of Barclay in Scotland, Keith was coauthor of religious tracts, and was no stranger to a prison cell because of his religious beliefs.

He had studied philosophy, mathematics, and ancient languages at Marischall College in Scotland, and became a tutor and later a surveyor. Born a Presbyterian,[30] he liked the Quaker concept of direct communion with God, but felt moved to clarify its rather vague theology. Active in the Edinburgh Friends Meeting, he began to suffer the official oppression so common to Friends and other dissenters: in 1663 he received his first prison sentence. His zeal was hardly tempered, however; in 1670 he visited England, where he met William Penn and other Quaker leaders. Returning to Scotland, Keith married a wealthy woman, resumed pamphleteering and speaking out, and continued to suffer the consequences: arrests, fines, and imprisonment.[31]

At last the opportunity presented itself for him to join other Quaker refugees in America. His friend Barclay, as governor of East Jersey, appointed him surveyor general in 1684 at two hundred

George Keith (1639?–1716), Surveyor General of East Jersey who ran the line dividing East and West Jersey in 1687. Also famed for his attempts to increase the orthodoxy of Quakerism, he later became an Anglican missionary to the colonies, as he appears in this portrait. *New Jersey Historical Society.*

pounds per year.[32] Keith arrived in (Perth) Amboy the following spring, acquiring fifteen hundred acres in Jersey and Pennsylvania. His fiery religious concerns again rose to the surface. By 1692, in the absence of Barclay's moderating influence, the impetuous crusader had created a serious rift among Friends in the colonies because of his increasing demands for orthodoxy, opposing the liberal, unstructured theology of most Friends in the then fifty-year-old sect.

Keith's attacks increased in bitterness. In June 1692, at the Friends' Philadelphia Quarterly Meeting, he was formally charged with treating the ministers "with vile words and abusive language" and as "fools, ignorant heathen, infidels, silly souls, lyars, hereticks," and so forth.[33] At the Yearly Meeting in September, he and his followers were condemned for their views. Amidst general censure by other Friends, the Keithians withdrew and formed a short-lived Christian Quaker sect.

Keith left for England in 1693 to plead his case to Friends there. The split was too deep, however, and he was disowned by London Yearly Meeting in 1695 after further provocations. The Anglican Church, quite evangelistic at the time, saw in him an ideal medium to reclaim Quakers. In 1700 he joined the Church, and was a priest by 1702.[34] In the same year he returned to America as an Anglican missionary and during his two-year stay was highly successful.

His work only widened the split in West Jersey, which, due also to immigration patterns, had changed from an essentially Quaker community in the early 1680's to a predominantly non-Quaker colony in two or three decades.[35]

JOHN WORLIDGE RUNS "AN EXACT SURVEY"— FOR 1700

The next attempt to portray the young colony on a published map was prepared about 1700 by John Thornton, a London hydrographer. Based on "an Exact Survey Taken by Mr. John Worlidge," it was entitled *A New Mapp of East and West New Jarsey*. It has the features of a finished map, but omits the embellishments of Blaeu, Visscher and Seller. The cartouche is a simple box in perspective. The only illustrations are simulated hills, not in hilly northwest Jersey, but in areas much flatter. Aside from a modestly designed compass rose, the emphasis is on information, not artistry.

East and West Jersey are divided with the 1676 Quintipartite deed line, but the map makes no reference to the Keith line of 1687. Also shown is a "line of partition between Burlington and Glocester Counteys" which appears to approximate a temporary line set up in 1692, but repealed a year later. On the other hand, no attempt is made to show the Jerseys' northern line with New York.

One other boundary appears for the first time: the zigzag northern line of "Dr. Daniel Cox Land," owned by the physician who had been absentee governor of West Jersey. Since 1845, this line has been the northern boundary of Mercer County. The "Exact Survey" could only have been intended for southern Jersey where Worlidge lived, and even there the latitude markings are about fifteen or twenty miles too far south. Ten inlets, two dozen creeks, several towns and two roads are identified in that area. The lands around Newark and Bergen are so inaccurately drawn that one wonders whether the surveyor was ever near there, and the north central area of the colony is totally devoid of detail north of the "Rariton R."

Worlidge himself lived in Salem. He was one of the 151 signers of the West Jersey Concessions and Agreements of 1677, and he surveyed, arbitrated disputes, and presided over at least one criminal court, which conducted a notorious murder case in 1692. When Worlidge died in 1698, his estate included four maps worth ten shillings.[36]

About the same time, John Reid prepared and R. Simson engraved a map which supplements the Thornton map by concentrating on the northeast Jersey area so neglected by Worlidge. Reid's map of *East Jarsey in America,* at 5 miles/inch, shows the Keith line from the "Mouth of Egg Harbour" "North and by West and three Degrees more Westerly," but without northern limit. Straight but askew dotted lines separate Middlesex from Essex and Monmouth Counties, and the "Hackingsack River" bounds "Berghen County." Much more detail and accuracy is present in this area, when contrasted with Thornton. Since Somerset County (formed 1688) is not mentioned, the map may have been drawn as early as 1687, the year of Keith's survey. If so, it is unfortunate that Thornton was unaware of it.

AN ARISTOCRAT BECOMES SURVEYOR GENERAL: JAMES ALEXANDER

A major influence in politics, civil and private boundaries, and general mapping development of New Jersey during the first half of the eighteenth century was its surveyor general. A Scottish-born aristocrat named James Alexander, he was the presumed heir to the Earldom of Stirling, but never assumed the title. Well educated and proficient in mathematics, he arrived in America in May 1715 at

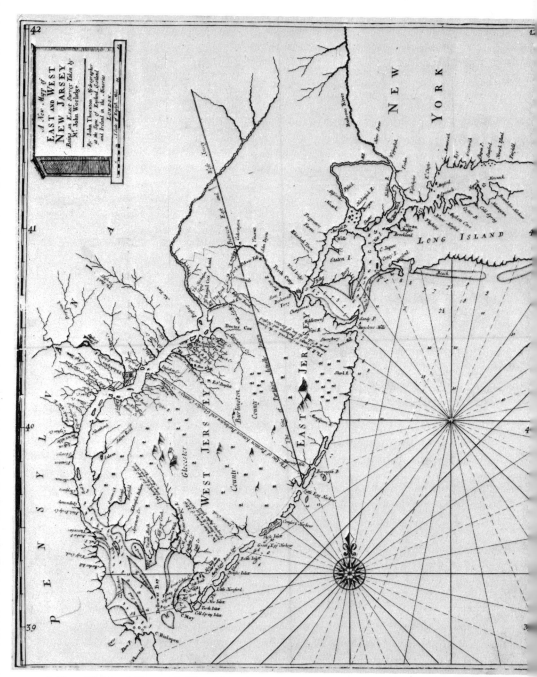

A New Mapp of East and West New Jarsey. By John Thornton, based on a survey by John Worlidge, ca. 1700. Worlidge's "Exact Survey" was obviously confined to south Jersey. The 1676 Quintipartite line, rather than the Keith line, is shown dividing the provinces. *Rutgers University Library.*

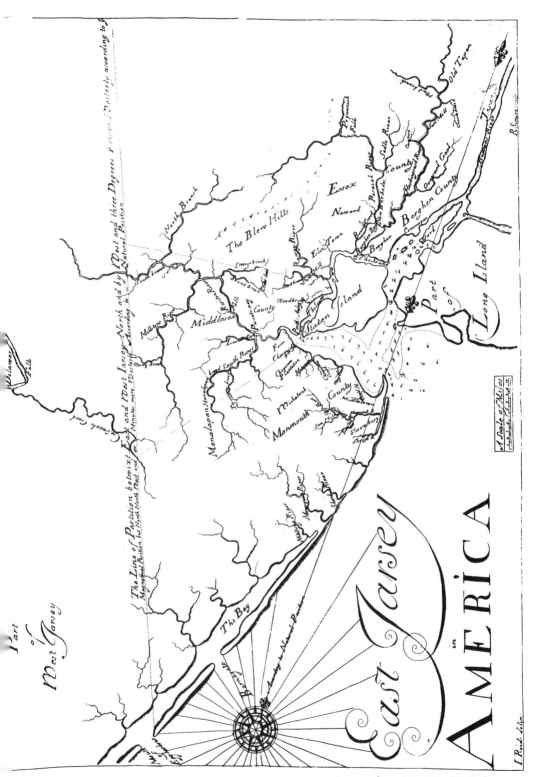

East Jarsey in America. By John Reid, ca. 1690. A map showing considerable detail in northeast Jersey, an area almost ignored by the contemporary Thornton-Worlidge map. *The Historical Society of Pennsylvania.*

the age of twenty-four, with a commission as surveyor general of both the Eastern and Western Divisions of New Jersey. The commission was granted by the London Board of Proprietors, with a letter from King George I, and it was confirmed for both East and West Jersey by the East Jersey Proprietors sitting in New York in October of the same year.

Alexander became a close friend and protégé of Robert Hunter, governor of both New Jersey and New York, and rapidly involved himself in high office and issues. In 1723 he received a seat in the New Jersey Council—the forerunner of the State Senate—and, as he did the post of surveyor general, held it until his death in 1756. From 1721 to 1723 he was attorney general of New York, and he held the same office in New Jersey during the next five years. He was also frequently a member of the Council of New York. His

James Alexander (1691–1756). Surveyor General of both East and West Jersey for 41 years, he wielded considerable influence in boundary disputes and politics. *Rutgers University Library.*

relations with governors of New York and New Jersey remained warm throughout his life, except for William Cosby. Cosby, governor of the two provinces from 1732 to 1736, developed such an intense dislike for Alexander that he fabricated charges that the surveyor general, while still in Scotland, had taken part in attempts to overthrow George I and the House of Hanover. Although the Common Council of New York City passed a resolution in 1736 attesting to his loyalty and character, the charge has been stated as fact in some historical accounts.

Alexander married a New York City merchant's daughter in 1725. She not only bore him four daughters and a son, but she remained in business in New York for many years. Their son William lived in Basking Ridge, assumed the title of Lord Stirling, and succeeded his father as surveyor general of the East Jersey Proprietors only. He also served in the New Jersey Council, 1761–75, and was a major general in the colonial army during the Revolution.

James Alexander himself drew few if any manuscript maps which still exist. The surveyor general was very active, however, in the attempts to resolve New Jersey's northern boundary in 1719, in the litigation surrounding the Elizabeth-Town Tract in 1747, in action against squatters in the Horseneck Purchase in northwest Essex County, and in numerous less famous disputes. With Benjamin Franklin, he helped found the American Philosophical Society, and he corresponded with European scientists such as Edmund Halley.[37] Hundreds of surveys run at his direction and other "Alexander Papers" are retained by the New-York Historical Society.

MAPPING FOR THE PROPERTY OWNER

The surveyors general were instrumental in subdividing the vast tracts acquired by the Proprietors of East and West Jersey from the Indians, and through the grant of the Duke of York. Transfer or conveyancing of the Proprietors' lands involved "severing" the title and followed carefully prescribed steps.

In West Jersey, the format was stated in Chapter 5 of "The Concessions and Agreements" signed by 151 inhabitants on March 3, 1676/77: The deputy was to survey

. . . Acres. of land for A B out of the several lotts of C D one of the Proprietors in the proportions following that is to say   part there of in the lott of the said C D in   which the Surveyor or his deputie shall lay out limitt and bound accordingly and shall certifie back to the Register on what point of the Compass the severall limitts thereof lie and on whose lands the severall parcells Butt and bound which last certificate shall be entered by the said Register or his deputie in a booke for that purpose with an Alphabeticall table of the Proprietors names and the name of the planter or purchaser referring to the said Certificate shall by the said Register be endorsed on the back of the grant with the folio of the booke in which it is entered and his name subscribed to the said Indorsement.[38]

James Alexander, during his long tenure as surveyor general for both divisions of New Jersey, prepared extensive instructions which he issued to deputy surveyors in both East and West Jersey. He discussed the variation of the magnetic compass, the use of stars to determine the compass error, and the taking of oaths ("or Affirmation if Quakers") as to survey accuracy.

Writing in September 1740 to the Eastern deputies, he provided a sample survey with rules for survey-map making:

. . . you'll find that I recommend

1st That all Corners or Ends of Lines be numbered 1, 2, 3, 4, 5 &c & so on which will Correspond with the field work

2d haveing chosen a North & South Line as NS in the Example Let all Courses be Set off by the help of parallalls (to that first Line) drawn from the End of Every Line _____ There be many other ways of protracting but by Experience I find this Least Lyable to mistakes . . . .

6th in the vacant places of your paper Set down the Coppy of your Computations of the Contents of every foursided or 3 Sided figure, as in the Example _____ Distinguishing the figure by the numbers at the Ends of the Lines thereof _____ Distinguishing the Common base by the two numbers at the Ends of it _____ & Distinguishing the perpendicular by the Single number from whence its Letfall or is taken to the base & Dotting the base near where the perpendiculars fall as in the Example . . . .

8 forget not the Scale . . . .

10 If you bound on a River Road &c without Sending Coppy of the field work therof, Youll give yourSelves & your Employers a Double

trouble for I will not make a Return where such boundary is without the field work & protraction by it.

Ja: Alexander Surv'r Genll.[39]

There are even now small tracts of land not severed from the Proprietors. Depending on whether the land lies east or west of the Lawrence line, the severance is handled somewhat differently. In West Jersey, the potential owner of such a tract must first determine its size, then purchase enough warrant rights from a holder of the right of propriety to cover the acreage involved. The Surveyor General then has a survey made and presents it for approval by the Council of Proprietors and recording by the Registrar. In either division, the new owner must also have it recorded by the County Clerk.[40] In East Jersey, the Board must first approve an application for a title. The Surveyor General is directed to make or order a survey, and the return of the survey is filed for Board approval and recording.[41]

Some of the early property surveys were also helpful in general map making, especially when several tract layouts were assembled into a composite map of a large area. Such eighteenth-century composites of portions of Sussex County near the Wallkill, of western Essex, and of the future Union County and northern Somerset may be seen in the New-York Historical Society. Later composites, especially of Morris County and shore areas, are held at the headquarters of the East or West Jersey Proprietors. Property maps of Somerset and Middlesex Counties, copied by John Hills, will be discussed later. One of the many manuscript maps of the controversial Elizabeth-Town tract (to be mentioned later) shows over a dozen successive Indian purchases from 1664 to 1717. At 150 chains/inch, the purchases are emphasized with colored outlines.

PATHS FOR THE TRAVELER

The early settlement of the eastern seaboard of North America was concentrated along the coast and along those waterways deep enough for the canoes, sloops, or sailboats of the early settlers and

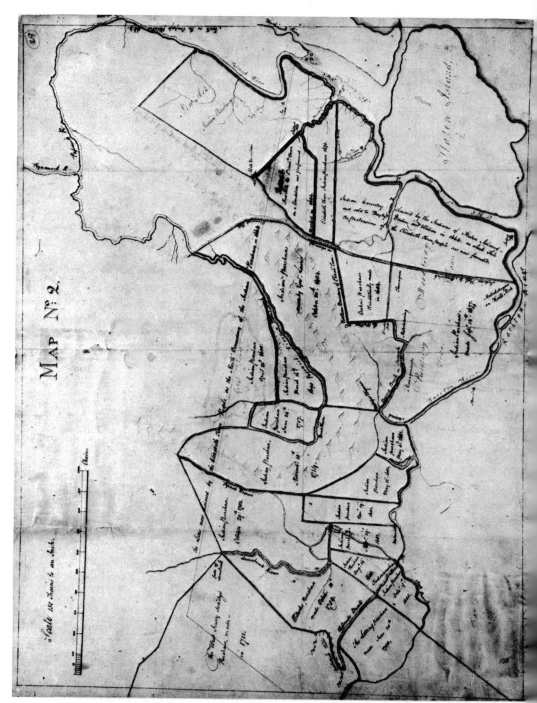

Anonymous map showing Indian purchases (1664–1717) in Elizabeth-Town tract. The ownership of this tract was the subject of extensive litigation in the mid-eighteenth century. *New-York Historical Society.*

merchants. Land travel was limited almost entirely to packhorse and horseback. Transportation over land was so unimportant that no published map of America showed roads until 1729,[42] when Herman Moll's map of *New England, New York, New Jersey and Pensilvania* showed the post road from Philadelphia to New Hampshire.

New Jersey was hardly without roads and trails, but few were included on maps. The Salem Road, from Burlington to Salem, and part of the road from New York to the "Delawar Falls" appeared on the Worlidge-Thornton map, but no others were shown.

Numerous Indian trails, such as the major Minisink, Burlington, and Cohansey Trails were well known, but were still just trails until travel became heavy enough to make conversion to roads essential. One other road was almost unknown to the English in the populated areas. This was supposed to have been built by the Dutch about 1650 along the Delaware River, starting from copper and quartz mines near the Delaware Water Gap, and extending more than fifty miles to Esopus, now Kingston, on the Hudson. There is growing suspicion that the road's origin may not have been this early or for this purpose, but portions of it are still in use between Pahaquarry and Montague Townships, and it is familiarly called the "Old Mine Road."

The legislatures set up Road Boards and Highway Commissioners beginning in the 1680's. The capitals of East and West Jersey—Perth Amboy and Burlington—were connected in 1684 by a new thoroughfare called Lawrie's Road, after East Jersey's deputy governor at the time. Other roads were converted trails, but nearly all roads were rudimentary and were built with little knowledge of how to provide a firm roadbed.

Records of road surveys did not begin in earnest until about 1760 (1715 in Salem County) when the survey "returns" began to be sworn to and deposited in the courthouses. Now bound in Road Books *A, B,* etc., they contain metes and bounds but generally no maps. During the twentieth century, several counties have spent the time—sometimes aided in the 1930's by the federal Works Projects Administration—to index many of the returns on current road maps. Most roads existing during and before the Revolution, however, especially in south Jersey, followed routes which are unknown in detail.

Ferries naturally developed over major rivers at such places as

Communipaw (Jersey City), Inian's (New Brunswick), Cooper's (Camden), and Perth Amboy, to replace fords or canoe crossings. Bridges came more slowly. Wheeled competition with horseback was limited to carts, wagons, and stagewagons until about 1750, when the first coaches began to make their appearance in New Jersey.[43] It was still later that they were used as stages.

Thus roads became significant entries on maps only toward the middle of the eighteenth century.

JOHN LAWRENCE SURVEYS A LINE
SEVENTY YEARS LATE

The survey of the Quintipartite deed line of 1676 finally was made in 1743. Actually, the Proprietors of East and West Jersey had surrendered their rights of government to Queen Anne in 1702, and in that year the two provinces were united to form the royal province of New Jersey. Its governor was shared with New York until Jersey received its own in 1738.

The twenty-six years of separate direction of the two Jerseys were not so easily erased, however, and the East and West divisions continued to be dissimilar in many ways. The puritanical and more heterogeneous East Jersey was culturally different from the more homogeneous Quaker West Jersey of the early decades. The economy of the East was more town-oriented, with smaller acreages. The West leaned to vast estates. The separate metropolitan growths of New York and Philadelphia by themselves were polarizing factors.[44] As a concession to the differences, the capital of New Jersey from 1702 to 1790 was alternated, by law, between the earlier capitals of Perth Amboy and Burlington.

In any event, property rights depended upon clarifying the Proprietors' dividing line. In 1719 the legislatures of New York and New Jersey appointed commissioners who determined the "true" location of "Station Point," the northwest corner of New Jersey, assuming that the Duke of York intended to place the corner at 41° 40' north latitude on the Delaware. One of the commissioners for the western division of New Jersey was John Reading, Jr., who later served briefly as governor of the province. While staking out several private surveys in northwest Jersey during 1715 and 1716, he kept an informative journal describing natural scenery, rattlesnakes, and friendly Indians. In 1719 he recorded his survey of the windings of the Delaware River below Station Point. The notes were printed in 1915 by the New Jersey Historical Society.[45]

Hiring a surveyor to run the 1676 line, however, required funds which were not forthcoming until 1743, when John Lawrence of Monmouth County was engaged.[46] His random line from south to north was followed by his true line from north to south in the fall of that year. His field book tersely describes his measurements and markers in the language of chains and links. With these notes, he began the true line on October 21st:

Began where the random line crossed Delaware River at the end of 114 m. 58 ch., thence run a perpendicular N. 80¼ E. 69, 10 L. to the true line. Course N. 9.19 W. 22 ch. The 115th mile an Elm about 1 foot diameter into a small bushy gully. Running S. 9,19 E. 66 ch. from the 115th mile. Flatbrook about 50 Ls. wide, a pleasant stream; course S. 9,19 E.

114 [mi.] A forked White Oak about 3 feet diameter, 14 ch. southerly of Flatbrook in the low lands on the Northerly side of the Pahaqualin Mountain.

113 A pine ab't 1 foot diameter, 45 Ls. west of the line on Northerly side of the mountain.

112 A Spanish Oak ab't 1 foot diameter, on the Northerly side of the mountain.

111 In the edge of a pond on the S. side of the mountain.[47]

The Lawrence line has persisted to the present day in resolving land titles. It appears on several maps issued throughout the last two centuries. The shift of the northwest corner of the province, when the northern line was finally settled in 1769, did not lead to a change in the Lawrence line, although West Jersey Proprietors vigorously tried to shift it for their benefit.

John Lawrence made numerous other surveys in East Jersey. Among the most interesting still in existence is a property survey at 100 chains (1¼ miles)/inch along the Jersey shore between the Manasquan River and Little Egg Harbor. Crediting the assistance of other maps, Lawrence showed both the Keith line of 1687 "the Course N by W 3° & 5' Westerly" and his own random line of 1743 at "N 9° 45' W." [48]

With others he signed a survey at a ½ mile/inch of "7500 Acres
of Land Survey'd for William Penn." Dated 1741, this tract lay in
Somerset County west of the Passaic River and of a branch of the
Dead River.[49]

Also in 1741, at the 100-chain scale, Lawrence prepared a survey
of the Elizabeth-Town tract, showing proposed boundaries with
Newark. He covered in detail the area from Newark Bay to the
North Branch of the Raritan, lying between the Passaic and Raritan
Rivers.[50] This was one of numerous maps issued as part of a celebrated suit by conflicting landowners in Elizabeth-Town. Usually
known as the "Elizabeth-Town Bill in Chancery," the suit was never
adjudicated.

The suit led, however, to an amazingly detailed document prepared
by James Alexander. When he filed the bill in 1745, it was written
on both sides of eighteen large parchment skins, each over two feet
square. To broaden the readership, Alexander arranged for its printing by James Parker of New York. Three maps, prepared by Alexander, were at first to be included as hand-drawn copies by Lewis
Evans. It was fallaciously concluded that it would cost only slightly
more to have the maps engraved on copper. The engraving was contracted for in spite of the high cost and was expertly done by James
Turner of Boston. Two maps were based on Alexander's own maps,
and the third was based on a reduced scale draft by Evans.[51] The
volume appeared in 1747 with the three engraved maps. The maps
progressively focus on the property in question. The first map shows
the Eastern seacoast from Cape Hatteras to Boston at about 40
miles/inch, showing little of Jersey except for its two capitals, Fort
Elsinburg, the York Road, and the Lawrence line.

The second Alexander-Turner map, at 5 miles/inch, outlines
Jersey north of Burlington. The "Upper" and "Lower" roads from
the Delaware River to New York cross the province in one direction,
and the Minisink Path of the Indians from Minisink Island to the
Navesink River near Shrewsbury crosses almost perpendicularly.
The Lawrence line, the counties (without boundaries), main towns,
several rivers, and some proposed northern boundaries are included,
but the rivers and the three roads are shown in a generalized manner, with curves drawn with more artistry than precision. Map No.
3 details property boundaries in the Elizabeth-Town tract between
Cushetunk Mountain and the Rahway River north of the Raritan.

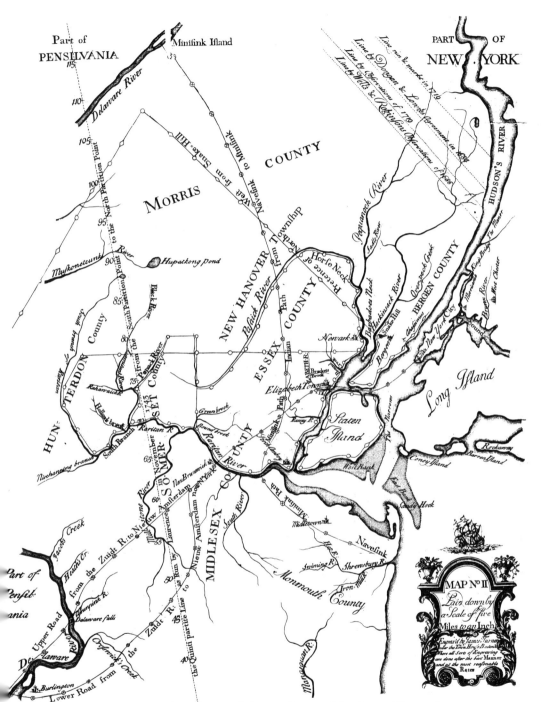

Map No. II, showing north and central Jersey. Engraved by James Turner from manuscript map by James Alexander, 1747, and included in the publication of the "Elizabeth-Town Bill in Chancery." *Rutgers University Library.*

Here the scale is 150 chains (1⅞ miles)/inch, and detailed surveys are evident.[52]

A map of the period which was not only amply supplied with artistic symbols and an ornate cartouche, but was also printed chiefly in Latin (with some German), was a ca. 1748 engraving by Tobias Conrad Lotter. It is titled *Pensylvania, Nova Jersey et Nova York. . . .* There are numerous place names shown in New Jersey. Southern New England is also included, but it is squeezed into a space far smaller than its area merits.[53]

LEWIS EVANS STRESSES EXCELLENCE

At last appeared a cartographer whose dedication to accuracy produced the first map of New Jersey and its bordering provinces which could be called reasonably accurate. Lewis Evans was a Philadelphian well acquainted with Benjamin Franklin. Evans was born about 1700 in Caernarvonshire, Wales, and he traveled to India and South America as a young man. Although it is not certain when he arrived in North America, he was established in Pennsylvania by 1736. He married in 1744, and Franklin's wife stood as godmother at the christening of their daughter. His wife died in 1748.

Evans was no stranger to political controversy, and he sharply attacked some of Pennsylvania's political leaders. Of William Penn, he publicly declared that "there is good reason to believe that W. Penn was not a real good Quaker at heart," due to his closeness with Catholic King James II. In a much more inflammatory accusation, Evans charged the governor of Pennsylvania, Robert Hunter Morris, who was also one of New Jersey's chief justices, with high treason. For his own safety after this charge, Evans fled to New York. The governor sued him for slander, and Evans was held in jail awaiting trial until released on a writ of habeas corpus just three days before his death in 1756.

In 1757 a New York historian, William Smith, wrote that Evans was "a Man in low circumstances, his Temper precipitate, of violent passions, great Vanity and rude Manners. He pretended to the knowledge of everything, and yet had very little learning." In spite of this, if the portrayal is accurate, Evans remained a friend until his death of both Franklin and the influential Thomas Pownall, who was a geographer, lieutenant-governor of New Jersey in 1757 and a governor in other colonies.[54]

A keen student of natural phenomena, a traveler and a surveyor, Evans kept detailed journals. His journal, for example, of a trip in 1743 from Philadelphia to Onondaga, included not only descriptions of the topography and rocks, but also complex theories of the formation of the mountain ranges. For some of his reasoning he referred to a set of Chinese geography volumes of the early seventeenth century! His theories concerning electricity astounded contemporaries.[55]

Most important of all, he produced two maps. In 1749, he published *A Map of Pensilvania, New-Jersey, New-York, And the Three Delaware Counties*. At a scale of 16 miles/inch, the map at last shows —crudely—the county lines of New Jersey. In addition to towns, inlets, and rivers common to earlier maps, Evans's map shows several roads, "Keith's Line 1687," and "The Division Line of East & West Jersey run in 1743." His depiction of Jersey's northern boundary as the line running from Station Point provoked a published criticism by an Orange Co., N.Y., resident, who felt that New York was wrongly deprived of land. He accused Evans of listening too attentively to a biased Jersey surveyor general, but Evans replied that he was merely marking a well-established boundary. If it was incorrect, he said, what *was* correct? [56]

Evans presented an outline of New Jersey which is actually more accurate than that of the later, much better-known Faden map of 1777, though the latter is more detailed. Evans's map was among the earliest printed in America, and is believed to have come from the Philadelphia press of Benjamin Franklin.[57]

After a second edition in 1752, Evans used his four-province map as source material for his celebrated *A general Map of the Middle British Colonies in America* . . . . Engraved in Philadelphia, published in 1755, and sold in both London and Philadelphia, the map embodies several improvements. For example, as Evans modestly points out,

In the first Impression [1749] of my former Map I committed some Mistakes in the Names of Places near the Entrance of Delaware Bay on the

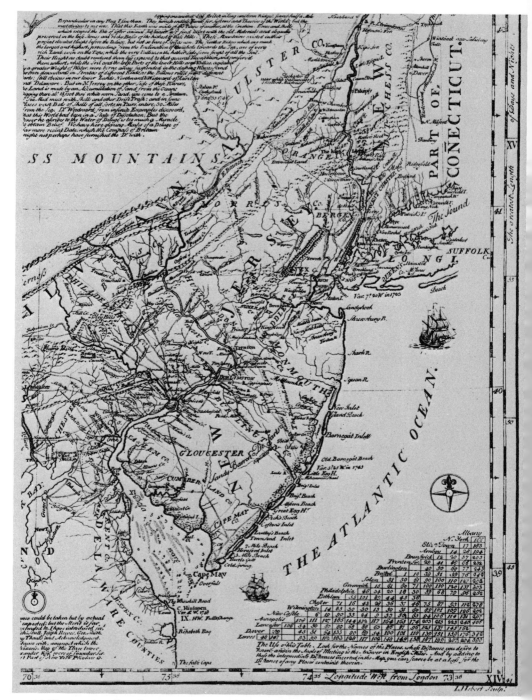

A Map of Pensilvania, New-Jersey, New-York, And the Three Delaware Counties, detail.
By Lewis Evans, 1749. New Jersey's claim line to Station Point is shown dividing the
province from New York in this much improved portrayal of the colonies. *Princeton
University Library.*

West Side and in my Attempt to rectify them, in the second Edition [1752], did but add to the Confusion. I have since had an Opportunity of making a thorough Enquiry into this Affair. . . .[58]

He did not list any errors found in New Jersey. The 1755 map includes all of Virginia, lower New England, and much of the future Northwest Territory and Kentucky. It profoundly influenced many subsequent maps of the area.

Since the area of the 1749 map was reduced in scale for this larger map, the detail suffers. County names and boundaries were eliminated, as were the Keith and Lawrence lines, and perhaps half the towns and rivers. But, as he removed a dozen river names in northwest Jersey, he added a half dozen communities in that area which may have been unknown to him six years earlier—Sussex, Walpack, Norton, Philipsburg, Wippany, and Sidney. There are only a few less roads.

A map so outstanding was likely to be copied, and Evans's map of 1755 was plagiarized and often poorly copied, though credited to Evans, in fifteen editions.[59] A copy in the library of the New Jersey Historical Society is not an Evans original, but one "Corrected and Improved . . . by Thos. Jefferys Geographer to the King" in 1758.

Thomas Pownall was outraged by this edition. In a tone proving that map making can be as controversial as politics, he declared that

A pirated Copy of this Map, soon after it came to England, was in a most audacious Manner published by the late Thomas Jefferys, under a false Pretence of Improvements, Lewis Evans's Name was put to it; and this Plagiarism was falsely sold as Evans's Map improved; by which that very laborious and ingenious, but poor Man, was deprived of the Benefit of his Work. The Engraver was so totally ignorant of the Principles on which the Original was formed, that although he traced the Lines of the Rivers and Roads in the usual Way, yet it can scarce be called a Copy.

The Mountains in America, which give the real Features to the Face of it, run in Ridges of a specific Direction, do in Places here and there run up into Peaks; do in others end abruptly in Knobs and Bluff-points; do interlock and have Gaps; all which Particulars were in the Original with a scrupulous Attention plotted and set down; as also the Parts where these Ridges spread into hilly Land. The Officer or the Geographer will look in vain for this Precision in the pirated Copy.

The blundering Copyist thought, that the filling the Places where he happened to meet with the Word, *Mountains,* with the Engraver's com-

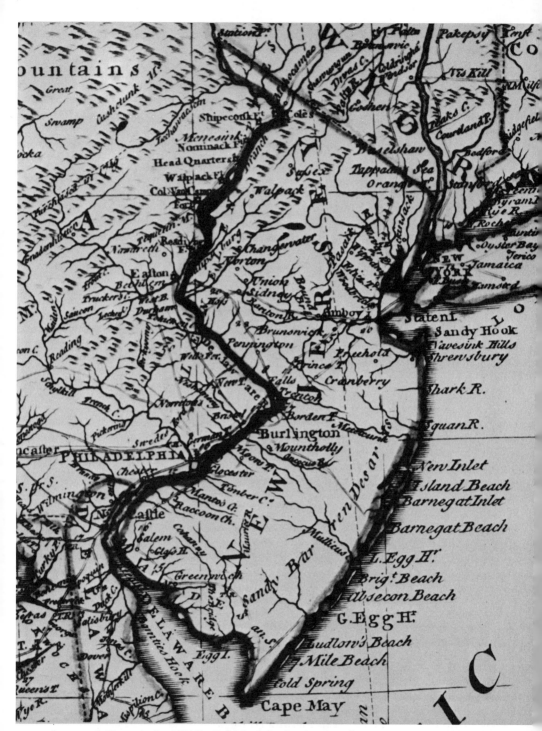

A general Map of the Middle British Colonies in America . . . ., New Jersey detail. 1758 revised copy by Thomas Jefferys of Lewis Evans's 1755 original classic. Nearly vertical dashed line shows magnetic north. *New Jersey Historical Society.*

mon Marks scratched in at random, was doing the Business, by which he has put Mountains where they are not; and has converted great Swamps into Mountains; and in other Parts has totally omitted the Marks of high Ground, because he did not understand those Marks which were used to express such high Ground, without presuming to give the Range and Form, where that was not yet known.

So far as respects the Face of the Country, this Thing of Jefferys might as well be a Map of the Face of the Moon. Further, in the Original there was observed a scrupulous Caution not to deceive; the Parts which were drawn from Report and Computation, and collected from Journals, are in the Original engraved in a slighter Manner, and very differently from those Parts which are laid down from actual Surveys; neither the Eye, the Ideas, nor the Spirit of the Copyist went to the Marking this; and all Parts stand equal in Authority in his false Copy.[60] [The paragraphing is the author's.]

With far more faithfulness to Evans's work, Pownall himself revised the 1755 map in 1776, secured its publication, largely from the original plate,[61] and essentially completed a further revision by 1784. The latter edition, still retaining the obsolete title *Middle British Colonies,* was not published at the time, but was reproduced as a marked-up 1776 map by the University of Pittsburgh Press in 1949. Pownall had updated New Jersey's northern boundary, but he retained a stippled line for the outmoded boundary claim to Station Point, and he added names of counties without boundaries.

SURVEYING WITH CHAIN AND STAKE

We may criticize the inaccuracies of these early maps, but in the eighteenth century it was no easy matter to survey. It still is not, but the modern-day surveyor has many conveniences unknown to his early counterpart. In looking back, Harold Barker, Jr., State Topographic Engineer, declared in 1965, "Considering the means at their disposal, the surveyors who produced earlier maps of New Jersey are to be admired for their perseverance. In fact, it is to their everlasting credit that they were able to do this work with any degree of accuracy with Jacob's staff, compass and chain." [62]

For centuries the most difficult phase of surveying was that nearly all the measurements had to be carried out on foot, with inclement weather, hilly terrains, and thick forests to be confronted as well as the problem of carrying chains, which were at the heart of line measurement. In the commission of 1743 to John Lawrence, some idea of the task—even on level ground—is indicated:

. . . you are to Direct the Chainbearers in Chaining to hold the Stick they are next to Put in the Ground in the same hand with the chain & within 3 or 4 Inches of the End that they are to Push in the Ground & to Stretch the Chain at Setting it in the Ground and to Direct the Marker to Mark the Trees . . . . You are to Cause every Tree which your Random Line cuts to be markt with three Notches on two Sides & Lett the Notches be as neerly as possible in the Places where the Line goes thro the Tree . . . and at the End of Each Mile Lett the Tree be markt with 3 Notches on the 4 Sides besides the Number of the Miles. . . .

After reaching Station Point, Lawrence was to run a series of perpendiculars between each mile tree of the random line and the true line, computing the course of the true line, "and for that Purpose you should Carry a Table of Logarithms with you in order to be Exact. . . ." After completing the fieldwork, he was "fairly to Lay down on a Map the Random & true Lines with all the Things you Observ'd in their true Places and make Return to Us of the Map and a Copy of your Field Work. . . ."[63]

The unit of measure was the chain. An official "chain" was 66 feet long and was divided into 100 links of 7.92 inches. Eighty chains constituted a mile of 5,280 feet. (The early Dutch used a shorter chain of 61' 11¾". Five Dutch rods made a chain, and a plot 25 rods by 24 rods comprised one "Morgen"—about two acres.)

In addition to distance, direction was essential. This was determined with the magnetic compass, which does not point true north because of the magnetic character of the earth itself, as well as localized variations due to magnetic ores. The compass error, called magnetic declination, varies from year to year and from place to place. In New Jersey the compass north has been west of true north throughout the last three centuries. In New York City it has varied from about 4° to its present 12°. In Philadelphia it has varied from 2° to 10°.

The bearings and distances thus measured were combined to produce the "metes and bounds" which have comprised the bulk of the

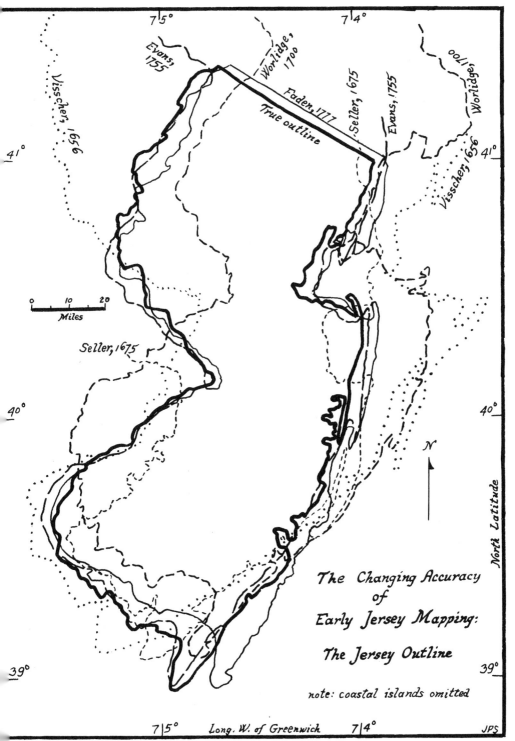

The changing accuracy of early Jersey mapping. In this composite of corresponding outlines of New Jersey according to early mappers, the latitude is as per the original map and the longitude of Philadelphia is held constant.

boundary descriptions in New Jersey. Early turning points were often trees or easily destroyed stakes: "a walnut stake that is pitched upon the plaine marked with two notches and a crosse" is part of the 1669 boundary of Woodbridge Township. Dr. Coxe's Hopewell tract, resurveyed in 1707, entailed a description resembling a proposal for a nature hike: ". . . a white oake Corner in the lowland & runs thence East South East fourty chain to a markt maple and hickery for a corner . . . ." Warren County's boundary of 1824 included another type of temporary marker: ". . . and running from thence, a straight course to the northeast corner of the Hardwick church . . . ." [64]

Hopeful signs were appearing. The 1773 law describing the new northern boundary of New Jersey required "stone monuments, at 1 mile distance from each other, along the said line, and to number such monuments with the number of miles." [65] This practice increased, and although it may have slowed the survey, it increased the chances that it would not have to be repeated.

CHAPTER TWO

From Dependence to Self-Reliance: Mapping, 1750–1800

JOHN MITCHELL'S MAP AND A TREATY

One more pre-Revolutionary map of the entire Eastern seaboard deserves mention because of the amount of detail it shows for New Jersey. It is the "Mitchell map" of 1755. Entitled *A Map of the British and French Dominions in North America . . . ,* it was produced in London by John Mitchell, a native of England who had settled in Virginia about 1700. Although his famous map was apparently his only cartographic work, he was also an accomplished botanist and physician. Mitchell collected numerous plant specimens while in America, and discovered several new species. As a physician, he wrote a treatise on yellow fever which was used during an outbreak of the disease in Philadelphia some fifty years later. In 1748 Mitchell returned to England, where he died after twenty years. He is believed to have written several published accounts of America and its relation to Great Britain's political future.[1]

Mitchell's map was not only used for military strategy in the French and Indian and Revolutionary wars, but its second edition of the same year was the map used by the commissioners to establish boundaries in the 1783 peace treaty between Great Britain and the United States. The map's errors in the northeast precipitated sixty years of dispute between Maine and Canada. Its inaccuracies in the northern limits of the Mississippi River led to confusion in the U.S.–Canada boundary at the Lake of the Woods which was not finally resolved until 1925.[2] Drawn to a once popular (and easily plotted) map projection called the converging meridian, it distorts shapes more

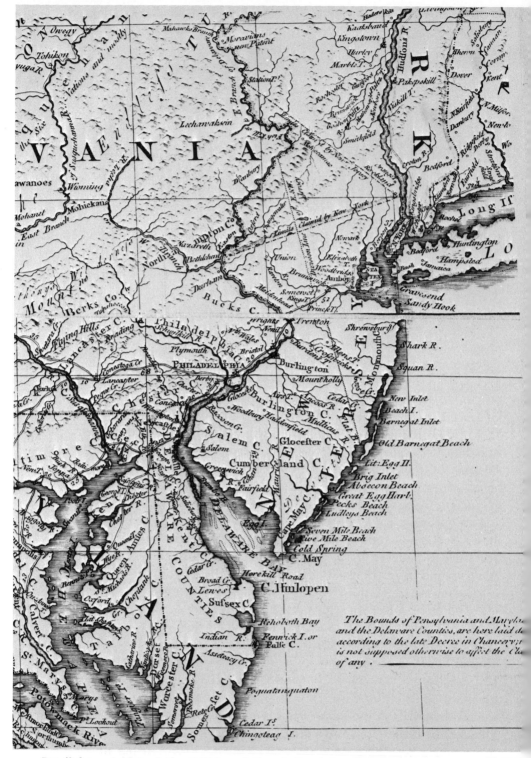

Detail from *A Map of the British and French Dominions in North America . . .*, by
John Mitchell, 1755. This British map was used to establish boundaries of the new
United States in the treaty of 1783. As with Visscher's map, its inaccuracies led to long-
term boundary disputes, this time between the U.S. and England or Canada. *Geography
and Map Division, Library of Congress.*

than necessary because it shows most meridians and parallels intersecting at the wrong angle. (Evans's map of the same year was drawn to the much more satisfactory conic projection, in which all the intersections are correctly made at right angles.)

Mitchell clearly shows the limits of both the New York and New Jersey claims concerning the northern boundary of Jersey prior to its settlement in 1769. Once again is shown the Lawrence line of 1743. Towns such as Newark, "Elizabeth T.," Haddonfield and Greenwich appear in printing of equal size. The six southern counties are named but unbounded. The seven northern counties are completely unmarked.

Whereas Evans used the longitude of Philadelphia as a starting point, Mitchell measured from the longitude of Greenwich, England —our current prime meridian. Careful scrutiny of Mitchell's New Jersey makes it evident that he did not rely heavily on Evans's 1749 classic. In fact, since Mitchell's map is inferior in some ways, he may not have even been aware of Evans.

It should be stressed that the improvement in New Jersey mapping by Evans and Mitchell was not universal. A 1759 map of *Nova Anglia* by the German cartographer Johann Baptist Homann contains a Jersey outline very much like the crude Visscher conception. East and West New "Jarsey" are shown separated by a wavy line about equidistant from the Jersey shore and the Delaware River, and Indian tribes are shown in abundance throughout the province.[3] Amazingly enough, one version of the Visscher (or was it Jansson?) map was still current in 1781.[4]

Another large map of the Middle Atlantic area appeared about 1768, entitled *The Provinces of New York and New Jersey with part of Pensilvania and the Governments of Trois Rivieres, and Montreal.* At a scale of about 10 miles/inch, the map was engraved by Thomas Jefferys, who credited Captain Samuel Holland as the author. Holland's involvement is questionable. British surveyor general for the Northern district of America and a member of the commission settling the northern boundary of New Jersey in 1769, Holland publicly disclaimed "Consent to the publishing of any Plan, Map, or Survey now extant, that bears my Name."[5] The map shows more detail for New York and Pennsylvania than for New Jersey. Three northern boundaries are shown for Jersey: its own claim to Station Point, the New York claim to the Lehigh River, and the

"Jurisdiction Line between New York and New Jersey for upwards of 50 Years" halfway between the other two and extending to Minisink Island. Seven of the thirteen counties are named, but are shown without boundaries.[6] Nothing significant is added to Evans's work. A 1776 revision appeared in Jefferys's *The American Atlas,* published in London by Sayer and Bennett.[7]

THE LOCAL SURVEYS

Obviously, map makers of the province relied on the work of others when they were aware of it and considered it reliable. Increasingly, there were accurate local surveys and maps, aside from property surveys, involving roads or settlements.

John Dalley of Kingston, N.J., surveyed the road from Trenton to Perth Amboy in 1745 and advertised in *The Pennsylvania Gazette* for subscribers to extend the survey and to prepare a map covering the entire route from New York to Philadelphia. All that ever appeared were colored manuscript copies of his Trenton-to-Amboy survey—indicating a shortage of subscribers. Of existing copies, one is inscribed to James Alexander, another to Chief Justice Robert Hunter Morris.[8] In 1762, Gerard Bancker copied the survey, giving full credit.[9] The scale of the maps is 1 mile/inch. Numerous dwellings are shown along the route, their symbol resembling the end view of a box-shaped house complete with peaked roof and two chimneys. Groups of houses and churches have their own symbols. Neatly inked in script are the names: homeowners, brooks, and legend. Towns and counties rate large roman print. The Keith and Lawrence lines are shown crossing the road, as if parallel, although actually converging. The mileage between any two of fifteen points is shown in a lined table similar to those on modern road maps.

A second manuscript map recently reproduced, like the Bancker copy, by Princeton University Library shows a boundary line surveyed by Azariah Dunham of New Brunswick in 1766. In 1714, the provincial legislature had declared that the boundary between Somerset and Middlesex Counties from the road at Inian's ferry in New Brunswick was to follow the "said old road by Jedediah Higgens's house, leading toward the falls of Delaware" to the Keith line.[10] The

Justice and Freeholders of Middlesex County ordered the 1766 survey in view of the fact that the "line of the old road" was "very dubious by reason of persons altering the road." Dunham, the surveyor, often served as an arbitrator of disputes in Middlesex County courts. Born in Piscataway in 1719, he was elected to the General Assembly in 1775, but quickly became involved in the Provincial Congress. During the Revolution, he supported the colonists in several leadership roles on both state and county levels. He died in 1790.[11]

Dunham's map shows the new road as well as the boundary—the two coinciding only in part. The fifty-year-old boundary line was identified with a series of black oaks, white oaks, a hickory, a chestnut, and an apple tree when it deviated from the new road. The legislature solved the problem of the increasing obscurity of the winding old boundary by moving the line to the center of the "main six rod road" in 1790.[12]

Azariah Dunham (1719–1790), prominent surveyor who was also a New Jersey assemblyman and an active Revolutionary leader. *Rutgers University Library.*

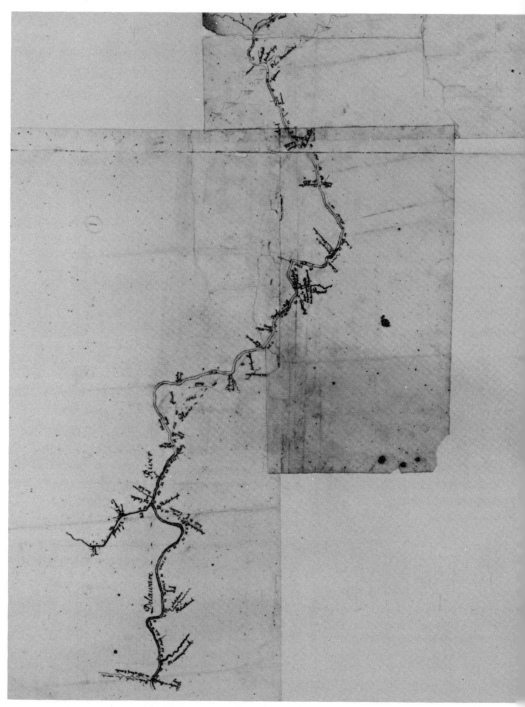

Detail from survey of upper Delaware River by Anthony Dennis, 1769. The river is shown from the mouth of the Musconetcong to the Delaware Water Gap. *New-York Historical Society.*

In 1769 Anthony Dennis made an extensive and detailed survey of the upper Delaware River from the Musconetcong River north to the "Upper Fork of Delaware" just below the 42nd parallel of latitude. At a scale of about 100 chains (1¼ miles)/inch, his survey is drawn on small sheets of paper which have been spliced by the New-York Historical Society into a strip map about seven feet long.[13]

A significant map of a large area is a manuscript map of almost the entire future Hudson County. Surveyed in 1767, the map was drawn anonymously at a scale of only ¼ mile (20 chains)/inch, showing roads and the larger property lines. Robert Erskine added a longitude and latitude grid and a table of mileages in 1779.[14]

Bergen Township, the eastern portion of the same area, received much closer attention in 1764, when seven commissioners were appointed to resurvey and clarify the numerous land titles developing from the original Dutch grant of 1630 to Michiel Pauw. Prompted by decades of uncertainties and encroachments, the commissioners established the ownership on maps and in large manuscript "Field Books," the latter of which were published with copious notes a century later. Among the seven were Azariah Dunham and Abraham Clark, Jr., a signer of the Declaration of Independence.[15] A composite property map of the township, signed by the commissioners, was prepared at a scale of 20 chains/inch, with an inset of Bergen village at 4 chains/inch.[16]

WILLIAM FADEN PRODUCES A CLASSIC

The Evans and Mitchell maps of the New Jersey area were relatively accurate but small. It remained for a larger, more detailed and more attractive (but somewhat less accurate) map of the province by William Faden to become the early Jersey map most popular to nineteenth- and twentieth-century New Jersey history enthusiasts. It is the best known and most frequently reprinted, but we cannot escape giving some of the credit for its popularity to its dates of 1777 and 1778 (revised)—in the midst of the Revolution—for many the climax of New Jersey history.

The Faden map, at about 7 miles/inch, followed a survey made in 1769 to assist the Boundary Commission in settling the century-old

The Province of New Jersey, Divided into East and West, commonly called The Jerseys. By William Faden, 1778. The second edition of a beautiful classic which is the most popular early map of New Jersey, in spite of its numerous inaccuracies of roads and boundaries. *New Jersey Historical Society.*

dispute between New York and New Jersey. The survey was ex-
ecuted by Bernard Ratzer, a Lieutenant in the Royal Artillery, who
prepared a simple map at 4 miles/inch from his findings: New Jersey was shown in outline, and a stippled line marked the road from
Paulus Hook to "Trentown," but the map was otherwise limited to
the boundary line and some survey lines and rivers in the area.[17]
Ratzer's map served as the basis for a smaller map of New Jersey at
10 miles/inch, showing only the Lawrence and Keith lines, the
northern boundary lines to Station Point and to the Neversink
River, and the natural boundaries of the province. The latter map
was included with the printing of an appeal for boundary clarifica-
tion submitted to the legislature by the Proprietors of East and West
Jersey in 1784.[18] Faden also refers to a survey by Bancker.

William Faden (1750–1836) was a prolific map maker of London
who succeeded Thomas Jefferys in business after the latter died in
1771. His fine engravings made him one of the greatest cartographers
of the late eighteenth century. He assembled map collections to suit
his customers, the number of pages in a given atlas varying widely.
His 1822 catalog listed over 350 publications.[19] Foremost was his
1777 *The North American Atlas, Selected from the Most Authentic
Maps, Charts, Plans, etc. Hitherto published*. It contains thirty-five
maps, concentrating along the eastern seaboard with detailed maps
of each province and colony from Quebec to Florida. A composite
map of North America extends to the southwestern portions of the
present United States, but omits the northwest and Latin America.[20]
North Jersey appears inadequately on his map of the province of
New York, and New York Bay is enlarged to show battles of 1776.
Map #22 is the one entitled *The Province of New Jersey, Divided
into East and West, commonly called The Jerseys*.

The completed map of New Jersey has errors of location ranging
to twelve miles,[21] and the western limits of the province (although
declared a state in 1776) are noticeably too sharp at the major bends.
Nevertheless, the map has a fine beauty which is emphasized in the
upper left corner by the attractive cartouche depicting a farmhouse
seen between two large graceful trees, and by the ranges of hills deli-
cately shaded as if illuminated from the northwest. The "Astronomical Observations" in the lower right corner add an exaggerated
sense of precision. The counties are outlined in red or yellow (de-

pending on the copy) with a larger border at the state line. Nearby colonies are outlined in green, blue, or yellow.

In addition to county lines and the new 1769 northern boundary, both the Keith and the Lawrence lines are shown, as well as numerous roads. The county boundaries are often seriously in error; Bergen County is limited by the Ramapo River according to the map, although it should have been extended to the present Passaic-Sussex line. The Morris-Sussex division is not shown at all, although it was described in a provincial law of 1753 and surveyed in 1758. Most other boundaries are rudimentary, the cartographer showing only mild awareness of the boundary laws already in existence in 1777. The lines, however, were the best-drawn to date, and they strongly influenced reconstructed maps drawn one and two centuries later.

Faden approximated the roads, showing them as nearly straight lines between towns, but there were few surveys to improve his accuracy. Certainly the Faden map was a pleasant step forward in New Jersey mapping. It merits a place of honor, even disregarding its Revolutionary date.

An interesting copy of Faden's map appeared in 1797. At first glance, the map appears to be almost identical, although the cartouche and astronomical observations are missing. A second look reveals the fact that the map is in German. Published in Hamburg, by C. E. Bohn, it was drawn by D. F. Sotzman, official cartographer to Baron von Steuben, the German warrior who aided the Americans during the Revolution.[22] Sotzman improved upon Faden's version of northern county boundaries, but he made few other changes.[23]

A very large map of northern Jersey appeared at about the same time as the Faden map. An unpublished manuscript map, it names neither author nor date, and is entitled "A Map of the Counties of Hunterdon, Sussex, Bergen, Essex and Morris also part of Middlesex and Somerset New Jersey And of the Counties of Orange and Ulster in the province of New York. . . ." It was probably drawn about 1775 or 1780. The only artificial county boundary shown is the line dividing Sussex from Bergen and Morris—even the Keith line is missing—but it is the most complete road map known of north Jersey for that period. Magnified by a scale of 2 miles/inch, the map shows an extensive network of red roads trimmed in black, with a limited accuracy far exceeding that of Faden's map. Rivers are colored blue; counties, where bounded, are bordered in green.[24]

Northern New Jersey, 1775. A reconstructed map showing townships and counties as they actually existed. © *John P. Snyder.*

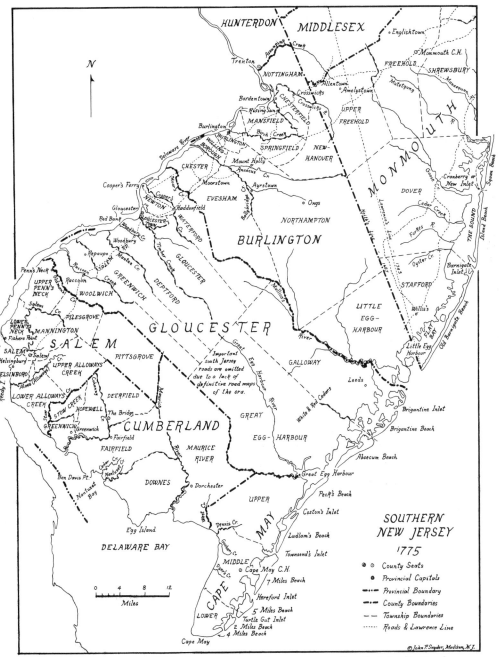

Southern New Jersey, 1775. Companion to the map opposite. © *John P. Snyder.*

Detail of "A Map of the Counties of Hunterdon, [etc.] New Jersey." Drawn at 2 mi./inch, the most complete road map of northern New Jersey, this anonymous manuscript map was prepared about 1775 or 1780. *New-York Historical Society.*

ROBERT ERSKINE BECOMES WASHINGTON'S SURVEYOR

New Jersey was intimately involved in the Revolution, although more reluctantly than some are willing to admit. Whereas some make the Revolution the heart of their interest in New Jersey history, the pathos of the war is only one of the many interesting stories of courage and tragedy for which New Jersey provided the settings during its three hundred years. The mapping of the region was neither seriously accelerated nor retarded by the war. The chief cartographic results were diversion to military surveys and the cutoff of British publishers.

There are three principal contributions to mapping of the province-state which were a direct result of the presence of troops in New Jersey. All are sets of military manuscript maps of roads: one a series of surveys chiefly made by Scottish-born Jerseyan Robert Erskine, the second a series prepared for the British army under General Clinton, and the third a set of on-the-spot sketches by the Frenchman Berthier. The greatest contribution—with respect to both accuracy and number of areas covered—was by Erskine.

Only one biography of Erskine has been written, and this was published in 1928 by its author, Albert H. Heusser. It was republished in 1966 by Rutgers University Press, under the editorship of Hubert G. Schmidt, who appropriately met the challenge presented by his conflicting desires. On the one hand, he wished to keep the hero-worshiping flavor of the rather homey 1928 story with its liberal use of suppositions. On the other hand, he hoped to improve the accuracy of the account.

Emerging from their combined efforts is a charming story [25] of one of New Jersey's own map makers, whose name is known to many who have visited Ringwood Manor State Park north of Wanaque Reservoir in Passaic County.

Robert Erskine was born in Dunfermline, Scotland, near Edinburgh, in 1735. (This was Andrew Carnegie's birthplace just a century later.) His father, a Presbyterian minister, died when the youth was seventeen. After some training at the University of Edinburgh about 1750, Erskine entered a partnership in 1759, apparently selling hardware and agricultural implements, in some cases to the American colonies. Unfortunately, his partner journeyed to the Carolinas with a considerable portion of the merchandise and thereupon disappeared, leaving Erskine bankrupt and facing the creditors alone. In 1762, the creditors filed suit, but the court released him on the condition that he attempt to repay them.

Erskine had patented a pump, which he now tried to commercialize. Again there were misfortunes, this time with the instrument maker whom he had hired to manufacture the pumps. He also invented a "Platometer . . . to find the Latitude & variation of the needle at Sea any time of the day by two observations of the Sun & any time of the night by taking the altitude of two known fixed Stars at the same time." [26] He was married in 1765, and in the same year he developed a "Centrifugal Hydraulic Engine" and another pumping system in 1766. For these and his other signs of prowess in the field of "mathematics and practical mechanics," he was awarded a fellowship in the Royal Society of London five years later.

In late 1769, Erskine began negotiations with some London investors who were on the verge of bankruptcy. They were victims of the ambitious extensions of their agent Peter Hasenclever, who was manager of several mines in north Jersey near the border, including Ringwood, Long Pond (Greenwood Lake) and Charlotteburg. The outcome changed the rest of his life: he was hired to manage the faltering complex. He spent two months in the fall of 1770 inspecting the mining regions and ironworks of England, Scotland, and Wales. Thus prepared for his new undertaking, he sailed for New York in mid-1771, arriving there in June.

Erskine lived at the Ringwood manor house—not the building now standing, but an older structure near it. His prestige was such that he was soon appointed a local magistrate, but his attempts to make Ringwood profitable were unsuccessful. So were his attempts to sell the enterprise in 1772. Losing backing in London, he borrowed from New York merchants, but by 1774 was left entirely to his own resources.

Meanwhile, as he saw the futility of colonists' appeals to England to retract oppressive legislation, Erskine increasingly sided with the colonists and organized one of New Jersey's first companies of militia in 1775. He was commissioned its captain. His engineering capabilities led to the invention of an underwater iron and wood structure which would prevent enemy ships from traveling up the Hudson. A few were installed, providing some income for him. Later, in 1777–78, his mines were among the sources of large iron links which formed barrier chains across the Hudson River at Peekskill and West Point.

In July 1777, Robert Erskine first met General Washington at Pompton (now Riverdale), N.J. As a result of the meeting, Erskine was commissioned the same month by the Continental Congress to be geographer and surveyor general to the Continental Army. In writing to Congress, Washington said,

A good Geographer to Survey the Roads and take Sketches of the Country where the Army is to Act would be extremely useful . . . . I would beg leave to recommend Mr. Robt. Erskine who is thoroughly skilled in this business, has already assisted us in making Maps of the Country; and has (as I am informed) uniformly supported the Character of a fast friend to America.[27]

In acknowledging the commission, Erskine replied to Washington with a number of graphic comments on the nature of the surveyor's work of that time:

It is obvious that in planning a country a great part of the ground must be walked over, particularly the banks of Rivers and Roads; as much of which may be traced and laid down in three hours as could be walked over in one; or in other words a Surveyor who can walk 15 miles a day may plan 5 miles; if the country is open, and stations of considerable length can be obtained, then perhaps greater dispatch can be made; very little more, however, in general can be expected; if it is considered that the Surveyor, besides attending to the course and measuring the distance of the way he is traversing, should at all convenient places where he can see around him, take observations and angles to Mountains, hills, steeples, houses and other objects which present themselves, in order to fix their site; to correct his work; and to facilitate its being connected with other Surveys. A Surveyor might go to work with two Chain-bearers and himself; but in this case he must carry his own instruments, and some of them must frequently traverse the ground three times over at least; therefore, to prevent this inconvenience and delay, as men enough can be had from Camp without additional expense, six attendants to each surveyor will be proper; to wit, two Chain-bearers, one to carry the

Instrument, and three to hold flag staffs; two flags, indeed, are only wanted in common; but three are necessary for running a straight line with dispatch; and the third flag may be usefully employed in several cases besides. From what one Surveyor can do, it will therefore appear that in making a plan, like all other business, the more hands are employed in it, the sooner it may be accomplished; likewise, that the director of the Surveyors will have full employment in making general observations, and connecting the different surveys as they come in, upon one general Map; and, at any rate, that a correct plan must be a work of time.

A great deal however may be done towards the formation of an useful Map, by having some general outlines justly laid down; and the situation of some remarkable places accurately ascertained; from such data, other places may be pointed out, by information and computed distances; in such a manner as to give a tolerable idea of the Country; especially with the assistance of all the maps in being, which can be procured: and this, perhaps, is as much as can be expected, should plans be required to keep pace with the transitions of War.

Navigable Rivers, and those which cannot be easily forded, and likewise the capital roads, should be laid down with all the accuracy possible; but, in the Map of a country, the general course of fordable rivers need only be attended to; it not being practicable to express small windings but on large scale, the same accuracy not being required here which is necessary to ascertain the quantity and boundaries of private property. In general, therefore, the adjacence to, and intersection of, such rivers with roads, will determine their course with sufficient exactness: the situation of woods and mountains, too, may be remarked in a similar manner.

Young gentlemen of Mathematical genius, who are acquainted with the principles of Geometry, and who have a taste for drawing, would be the most proper assistants for a Geographer. Such, in a few days practice, may be made expert surveyors. The instrument best adaped for accuracy and dispatch is the Plain-Table; by this, the Surveyor plans as he proceeds, and—not having his work to protract in the evening—may attend the longer to it in the day. One of these instruments, with a chain and ten iron-shod arrows, should be provided for each of the Surveyors it may be thought proper to employ.[28]

Erskine emphasized the fact that he could not survey full-time because of his distracting business involvements.

Washington, a trained surveyor, did not disagree with his proposals. Erskine then proceeded to prepare over a hundred maps, about one-third involving New Jersey. Many of the maps consist of two to twenty sections on separate sheets. Several surveyors were involved, for example, Benjamin Lodge, John Armstrong, and William Scull, all officers of Pennsylvania regiments, and credited with from one to three of the maps.[29] (Not all of his subordinates' work pleased Erskine: On Map 79A, he wrote in a corner near Elizabethtown "This is surveyed by Mr. Lodge. . . . A Most abominably Lazy Slovenly Performance not to Survey such a small piece over again or lay it down properly. Witness RE$_{F.R.S.}$")

Erskine's chief assistant, and successor as surveyor general, was Simeon DeWitt, a New Yorker born in 1756 and Queen's College's (now Rutgers) sole graduate of 1776. After he joined the Continental Army, his uncle, a general, recommended him to Erskine. Since De-Witt prepared over a dozen of the military road surveys following Erskine's death, including roads from Philadelphia to Yorktown, Va., the set of surveys is usually called "Erskine-DeWitt." When the war was over, DeWitt tried to publish the maps, but failed.[30] From 1784 until his death fifty years later, he was surveyor general of New York State.

In 1780, a few months before his own death, Erskine reported that the number of assistant surveyors had varied from two to six (paid two or three dollars per day—he received four) but that he had averaged one assistant draftsman, three surveyors, and eighteen chain bearers.[31]

Erskine died in October 1780 at Ringwood. A cold and fever took his life at the age of forty-five. His widow remarried and, with her husband, retained control of Ringwood until 1783, when it was auctioned off. The property lay nearly dormant until 1807, when the Ryerson family bought it, soon replacing the old manor house with a new house which still stands.

Aside from the dip into southeastern Virginia, the Erskine-DeWitt maps show portions of Connecticut, New York, Pennsylvania and New Jersey. In Jersey they include "the principal part of New Jersey, lying northward of a line drawn from Sandy Hook to Philadelphia," to use his words.[32] Actually, most mapping fell in an area bounded by Ringwood, Phillipsburg, Trenton, and (Perth) Amboy, and especially in the triangle formed by Morristown, Elizabethtown and (New) Brunswick. A notable omission was the future Hudson County area. About a half dozen Jersey maps are missing. Essentially all of the rest are held by the New-York Historical Society in Manhattan, with photocopies of most of the sheets at the Morristown Na-

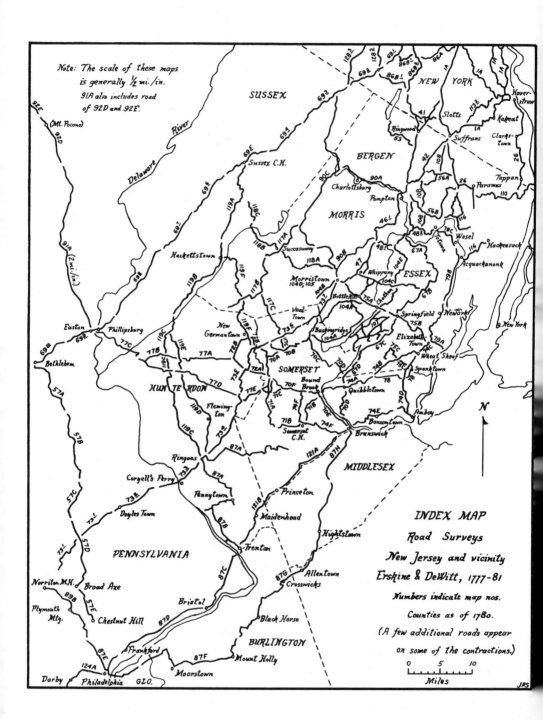

Note: The scale of these maps is generally ½ mi./in.
91A also includes road of 92D and 92E.

SUSSEX

NEW YORK

BERGEN

MORRIS

ESSEX

SOMERSET

HUNTERDON

MIDDLESEX

PENNSYLVANIA

BURLINGTON

N

INDEX MAP
Road Surveys
New Jersey and vicinity
Erskine & DeWitt, 1777-81
Numbers indicate map nos.
Counties as of 1780.
(A few additional roads appear
on some of the contractions.)

0   5   10
Miles

JRS

70

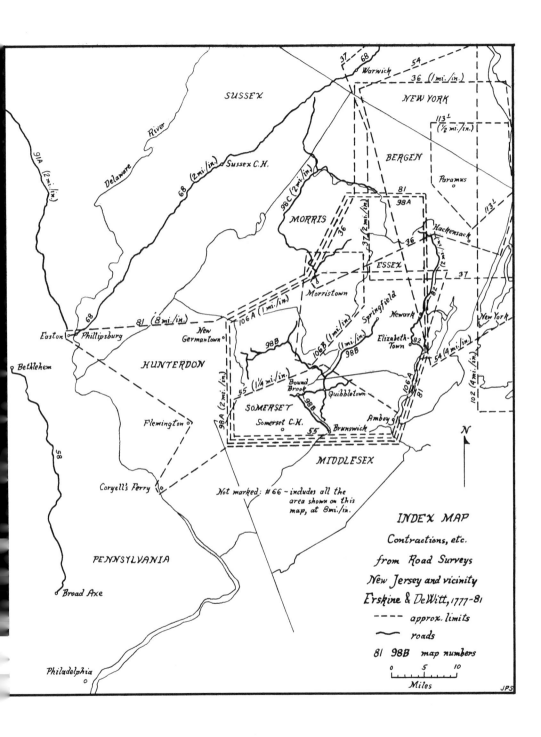

INDEX MAP

Contractions, etc.

from Road Surveys

New Jersey and vicinity

Erskine & DeWitt, 1777-81

- - - - approx. limits

——— roads

81 98B   map numbers

0   5   10

Miles

Not marked: #66 – includes all the
area shown on this
map, at 8mi./in.

71

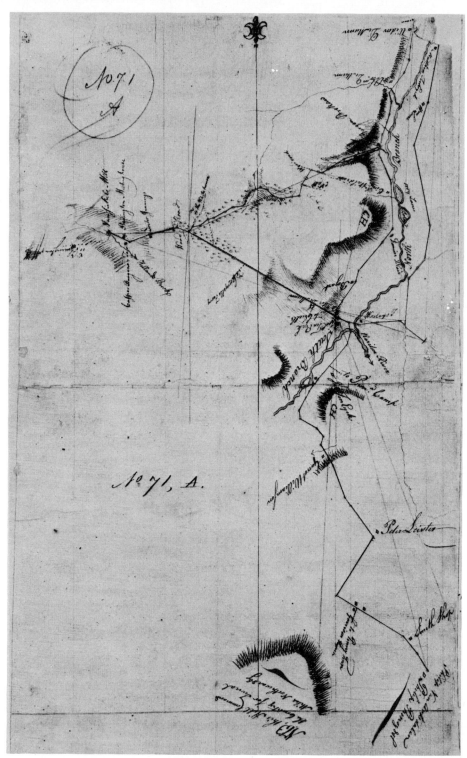

Map No. 71A, roads near the North Branch of the Raritan River in western Somerset County, surveyed in 1779 by Robert Erskine. An example of his road surveys made for General George Washington. *New-York Historical Society.*

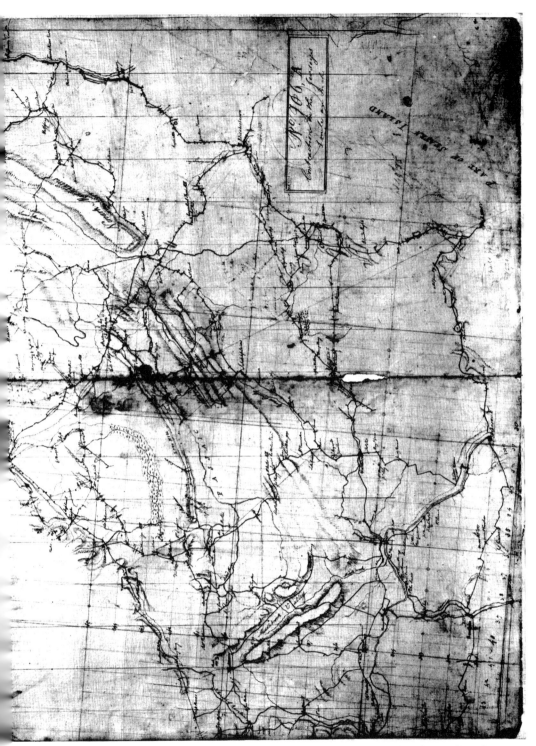

Map No. 106A, "Contraction in the Jerseys, 1 mile an Inch," probably by Simeon DeWitt. Much reduced, this 1780 map shows main roads in an area bounded by Morristown, Pluckemin, Somerset (Millstone), Perth Amboy, and Second River (Belleville). *New-York Historical Society.*

tional Historical Park Library, and of some at the libraries of Morristown and Rutgers.

Most of the maps were prepared as carefully drawn manuscript sketches without borders, and generally in script. The scale is unmarked, but consistently measures ½ mile/inch. Names are written in the direction most convenient to the draftsman, some completely upside down with respect to the title. What few extra copies there were had to be traced by hand from the original.[33] Roads are shown single-line as a series of connected straight lines between instrument setups. Householders are identified in rural areas; in towns the names are omitted. Using few symbols, Erskine preferred written descriptions.

Several other Erskine-DeWitt maps were neatly compiled from a number of field sketches, and were called "contractions." Smaller in scale, they range from 1 to 8 miles/inch and occasionally include large portions of New Jersey. Map No. 106A, for example, at 1 mile/inch covers with great care the area bounded by Morristown, Pluckemin, Somerset C. H. (Millstone), Perth Amboy, and Second River (Belleville). Some of the smaller-scale maps, with title blocks and borders, are lettered with neat roman print, but the roads—dotted —are only roughly shown.

The Erskine-DeWitt maps undoubtedly provide the most detailed information available about New Jersey roads during the Revolutionary war. They are so accurate that they can be superimposed over modern topographic maps of old roads still in use— and there are many—with only minor discrepancies.

MAPS FOR FRIEND AND FOE: BERTHIER AND THE "CLINTON MAPS"

The British army also required up-to-date road information in its futile attempts to stop the insurrection of the American colonies. After Sir William Howe was relieved as the British commander in May 1778, Sir Henry Clinton succeeded him and began a twelve-day march in June across New Jersey to evacuate his men from Philadelphia and march them to New York.

While en route he encountered General Charles Lee and his

colonial troops at Monmouth Court House (now Freehold). Lee was to attack Clinton's army at dawn, but he delayed several hours and then reconsidered after sending his men forward. Clinton was soon witnessing a premature retreat by Lee, until General Washington arrived with more men and condemned Lee's faintheartedness. Supplemented by Molly Pitcher's legendary courage in replacing her fallen husband at a cannon, Washington turned the battle of Monmouth into a costly defeat for the British and only a little less bloody victory for the colonists.[34]

Over thirty maps covering large and small areas of New Jersey were prepared from new fieldwork, or were copied from earlier surveys, and used by General Clinton's army. Large property maps of Somerset and Middlesex Counties were among them. Using a scale of 50 chains (⅝ mile)/inch, Lieutenant John (printed "Iohn") Hills, an assistant engineer for Clinton, copied them from surveys of 1766 by Benjamin Morgan and Azariah Dunham, respectively. Most other "Clinton maps," as they are called, are unsigned manuscript maps which resemble Erskine's maps in style, but they are roughly drawn and apparently did not result from instrument surveys. The original maps are preserved at the William L. Clements Library of the University of Michigan, but Rutgers University Library and the Morristown National Historical Park have full-size photocopies of many of them.

The third set of military road maps of New Jersey, only six in number, was prepared by a twenty-eight-year-old officer on Rochambeau's French army staff. Louis-Alexandre Berthier (1753–1815), later to become a marshal and Napoleon's chief of staff, had been trained as a military cartographer, and he prepared the maps from field notes made as the army marched through the colonies from 1780 to 1782. The march through New Jersey, from Suffern, N.Y., to Trenton, occurred in August 1781, two months before the French assisted Washington in his victory at Yorktown.

Each map represents a day's march of about fourteen miles, but in contrast to Erskine's works, and like the Clinton maps, no survey is evident, and the accuracy suffers. The roads are double-line, curving paths, with houses marked, but only landmarks are named. With Berthier's practice of straightening out the general routes and showing them running from left to right, the direction of the completely missing north arrows would vary not only from map to map,

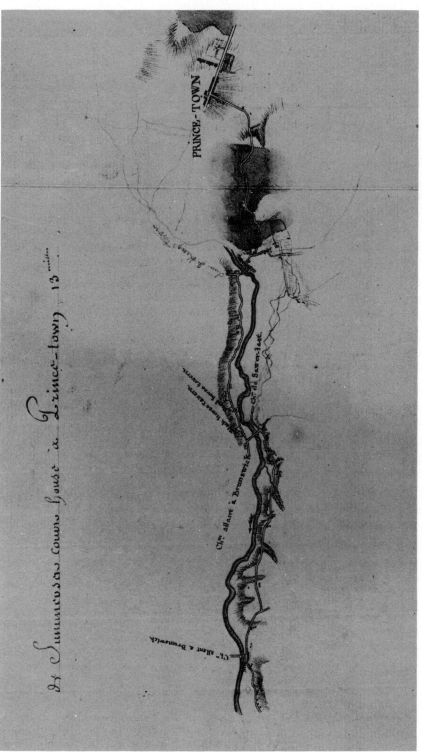

"From Somerset courthouse to Prince-town 13 miles," by Louis-Alexandre Berthier, 1781. One of his six maps based on field sketches of roads used by the French army under Rochambeau while traveling through New Jersey during the Revolution. *Princeton Uni-*

but from one part of the same map to another. Printing is in French; watercolors help to distinguish the features. Although they also lack borders and title-blocks, they are more artistic than Erskine's maps. In addition to the road maps, Berthier prepared a local map of the campsite at each of the overnight stops on the route. The return march in September 1782 followed the same route in reverse. The existing originals cover the route from Providence, R.I., to Head of Elk (Elkton), Md., campsites from Boston to Yorktown, and three fords—one at Trenton. They are held by the Princeton University Library, which reproduced the six Jersey maps in its 1964 booklet of road maps.[35]

ROADS AND TOLL BRIDGES

With independence declared in 1776 and effected by the treaty of 1783, New Jersey, like the other new states, was faced with two principal mapping needs: primary reliance on American map makers instead of British, and improvement in road maps to facilitate travel.

Stage-wagon routes of the 1740's had extended only within New Jersey, providing a four- or five-day trip from New York to Philadelphia. The stage boat had been especially uncertain, affected by winds and tide. New roads, improved ferries, and staunch competition between stages led to a two-day trip by 1766.[36] Five years later the time between the two cities had dwindled to a day and a half. Stage lines were also radiating in other directions from Newark and Paulus Hook—the link by ferry to New York—in the north, and from Cooper's Ferry (Camden), linking Philadelphia in the south.

The war, of course, caused general abandonment of regular stage-coach service, but military requirements only called more attention to the need for better roads.[37] The end of the war led to some of the needed activity, but the state could barely keep the roads in their prewar condition. Toll bridges over the Passaic and Hackensack Rivers, initially financed by lotteries, were authorized in 1790 and completed in five years. The Raritan was bridged at New Brunswick in the same year only after a flood and inexperienced workmen skyrocketed the cost to $86,000, far more than expected, and, as it turned out, beyond the point of economic payoff.[38] A toll bridge over the Delaware at Trenton was the most costly, and largest. Authorized in 1798, it was completed in 1806, at a cost of $180,000.

The toll bridges were only modestly successful in paying for themselves, but they helped inspire the next phase of road building in New Jersey—the toll road. Those all appeared after 1800, and will be discussed later.

THE ENGINEER WHO COULD NOT SUCCEED: CHRISTOPHER COLLES

The need for better road maps caught the interest of one man early in the life of the new nation. In 1789 Christopher Colles published the first set of road maps produced in the United States. Trying to appeal to the ordinary traveler, he was unable to make a commercial success of the publication.

Failure in business ventures was the perennial plight of Colles, even more so than it had been for Robert Erskine. Colles was born in Dublin in 1739. Specializing early in engineering, he worked with an uncle for several years on the building of a canal in Ireland. This was followed by restless years and varied jobs until his uncle died in 1770. With family responsibilities pressing him, he decided to try a new life in America and landed in Philadelphia in August 1771. This followed by two months the arrival of Erskine, whom he apparently never met.

In critical need of income, he first advertised as a machine designer, surveyor, architect, and private tutor of mathematics. Next he offered lectures on geography, physics, and mechanics, with some success. In 1773, he developed a special steam engine, and continued lecturing. He became intrigued with the need for a public water supply for New York City. Equipped with a complete design, he convinced the city of the need in 1774, and the system of deep wells, steam pumps, reservoir and bored pine pipes was well under construction when halted by the war two years later. Soon thereafter Colles, sympathetic to the colonists, fled New York City as the British army approached.

Colles and his family spent the war years, like many others, wan-

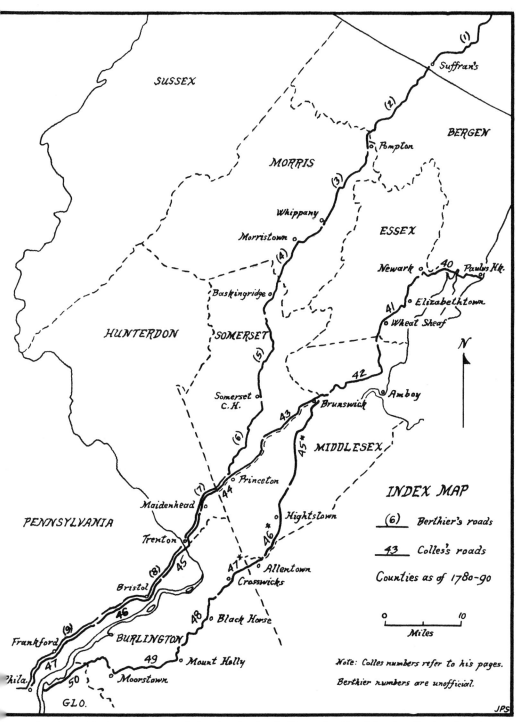

Index Map: (1) New Jersey road sketches by Louis-Alexandre Berthier, for Rochambeau's French army during their assistance to colonial troops in 1781. (2) New Jersey roads contained in Colles's *A Survey of the Roads of the United States of America*, 1789.

dering and seeking elusive employment. Briefly in New Jersey, he fled to Kingston, N.Y., and from there his odyssey is unknown. He is thought to have traversed the Hudson valley, eastern Pennsylvania, north Jersey and western Connecticut,[39] and was apparently never in the army.

In January 1783, however, he wrote a letter to George Washington. At the time, Colles lived in Morristown, N.J. He proposed that he be hired to improve the navigability of the Ohio River by removing some of the rapids. He gave three army officers as character references. Washington promptly replied that the idea was excellent, but premature, "from the present juvenile state of the Country, the abundance of land, the scarcity of labourers, and the want of resources." He suggested that Colles "turn your attention and abilities to works of more immediate public utility." [40]

Colles returned to New York City a year later, destitute and disappointed from the rejection of his Ohio River proposal. Applying the same idea to the Mohawk River, he received legislative support from New York, but this time could not raise the private funds he needed. He was ahead of his time: the Erie Canal along the Mohawk became a reality—after his death. Colles's last waterway plan consisted of an above-ground canal proposed in 1808. It was to cross New Jersey from Middle-town Point (now Keyport) to Burlington, as a link between New York and Philadelphia. When President Jefferson turned this down as impractical, Colles once again found a dream crushed. After disappointing efforts to promote other inventions, he died almost penniless in 1816 at the age of seventy-seven.

Hydraulic engineering was only one of Colles's fields of interest. Surveying was the field that led to his book of road maps and thereby to his greatest fame. He apparently conceived the idea of the road maps during the war. By 1789 he had prepared the set of eighty-three maps which constitute *A Survey of the Roads of the United States of America,* published in the same year. He had invented a new form of perambulator, which consisted of a large wheel pushed by the surveyor as it automatically counted the revolutions, which were readily convertible to distance traveled. This was much easier than laying heavy chains, but also subject to more inaccuracies. He probably used it in some of his surveying.

The *Survey* covers the main route—sometimes two alternate branches—between Albany, N.Y., and Yorktown, Va. An even dozen of the eighty-three maps are devoted to New Jersey: the road from Paulus Hook (Jersey City) to Philadelphia via Trenton and an alternate via Mount Holly.

Colles issued a broadside in 1789 calling for subscribers to his book. It was to be "neatly engraved on copper, each page containing a delineation of near 12 miles of road upon a scale of about one inch and three quarters to a mile," with numerous houses, shops, and other landmarks identified. Readers were optimistically told that "A traveller will here find so plain and circumstantial a description of

Christopher Colles (1739–1816), author of the first published set of road maps in America. An Irish-born engineer who emigrated to America in 1771, he was full of ideas for which he was unable to get enough support, often because they were twenty to forty years early. From a portrait by John Wesley Jarvis. *New-York Historical Society.*

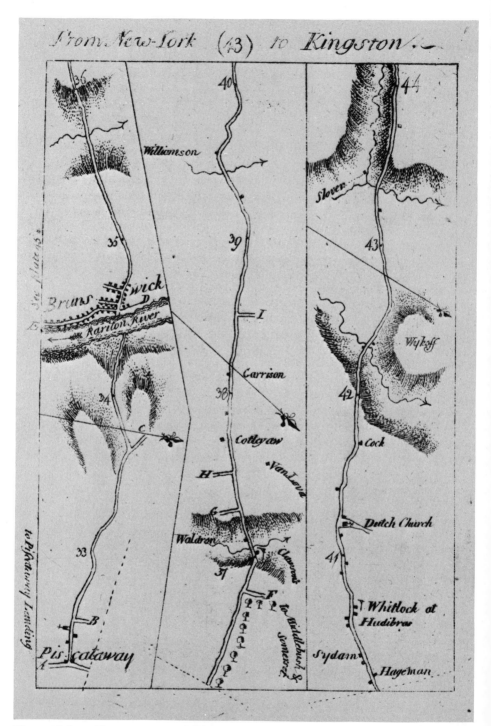

The road from Piscataway toward Kingston, Map #43 from Colles *Survey of the Roads,* 1789. Borrowing the strip chart principle used in England since 1675, he marked mileage (from New York on this map), landmarks and terrain. *Geography and Map Division, Library of Congress.*

the road, that whilst he has the draft with him it will be impossible for him to miss his way." He planned to have one hundred pages, but fell short, probably due to his perennial lack of subscriptions.[41] Failing to raise funds in this manner, Colles appealed next to the New York legislature, then to Congress. Rebuffed by both, he finally abandoned the project in the early 1790's.

There is little doubt that the Erskine-DeWitt maps played a significant role in over half of Colles's maps, in view of the similar features and names. One map librarian, a former Chief of the Library of Congress Map Division, concluded in 1937 that "Colles made none of the maps heretofore attributed to him as author." Others have not been so extreme in their judgments, but Walter W. Ristow found numerous examples of striking similarity, including several in the New Jersey area.[42] In any case, Colles engaged others to do the engraving. Cornelius Tiebout of New York was one engraver, so credited on the title page, but variations of style raise suspicions that he may not have been the only one.

The engraving of the maps was often uneven and amateurish. Colles was trying to sell a commodity little in demand until the early 1800's, when more professional guidebooks became available. He did not include any of New England except southwestern Connecticut. His maps were, however, easy to follow and represented the first American application of the strip charts which had been popular in England since their introduction in a 1675 road atlas by John Ogilby.[43]

At least fourteen complete copies and nine partial ones still exist in various libraries. The entire book was reproduced by Harvard University Press in 1961, and supplemented with a detailed biography of Colles prepared by Ristow.[44]

A GEOGRAPHER FROM NEW JERSEY: THOMAS HUTCHINS

The federal government began to undertake surveying and mapping at an early date, although the surveying was sporadic. New Jersey-born Thomas Hutchins played a prominent role in bringing about the Public Land Survey as the eighteenth century ended, by perfecting a system for plotting western territorial lands for sale by the government.

Hutchins was born in Monmouth County in 1730, and he spent his youth on the Pennsylvania frontier, later fighting in the French and Indian war and preparing the engineering plans for Fort Pitt and other fortifications. While an officer in the British army, he wrote travel journals and topographic descriptions of sufficient importance to earn him election to the American Philosophical Society in 1772. The Revolution led him to procolonial activity and imprisonment for several months by the British. On release in 1780, he resigned his commission, joined the colonial army, and became Geographer to the Southern Army under General Greene in 1781. Later the same year the title became Geographer to the United States.

For several years after the war he helped direct state boundary surveys and lay the gridwork for the Public Land Surveys. Hutchins died in 1789 while still in the midst of the latter work. He had contributed little to his native state, but much of value to his country.[45]

THE AMERICANIZATION OF NEW JERSEY MAPPING

One more outstanding map of part of New Jersey made its appearance just before the end of the eighteenth century. In October 1796 John Hills, signing himself as surveyor and draftsman of Philadelphia, issued a *Survey of part of the said State* of New Jersey and dedicated it to the Governor, Council, and Assembly. Drawn to a scale of 2 miles/inch, it shows only the counties of the eastern division (formerly East Jersey).

Hills's knowledge of Jersey decreased as he moved north: on his 1796 map, Monmouth County includes boundaries of all the townships and considerable additional detail, in Middlesex and Somerset most townships are identified, while Essex and Bergen Counties are shown without any marking of their ten townships, except for Bergen Township (presently eastern Hudson County). West Jersey is blank, but there is a detailed map of the Delaware River, listing mills and ferries, from Trenton north to the New York line. A rare

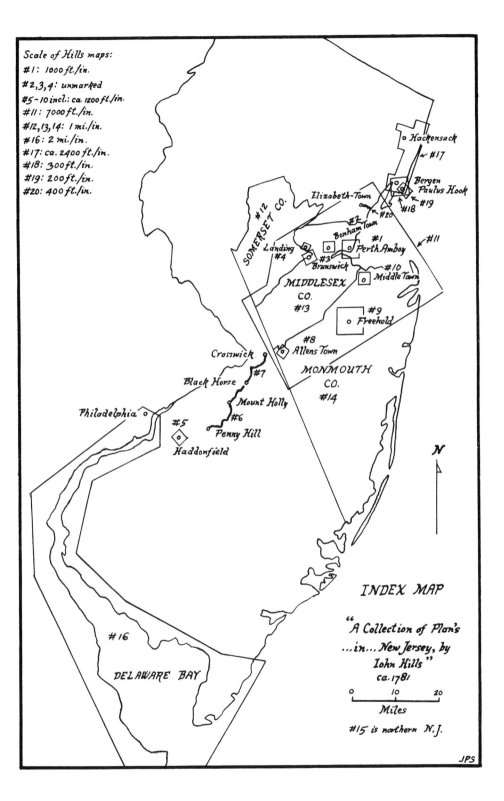

Scale of Hills maps:
#1: 1000 ft./in.
#2,3,4: unmarked
#5-10 incl.: ca. 1200 ft./in.
#11: 7000 ft./in.
#12,13,14: 1 mi./in.
#16: 2 mi./in.
#17: ca. 2400 ft./in.
#18: 300 ft./in.
#19: 200 ft./in.
#20: 400 ft./in.

Hackensack ←#17

Bergen
Paulus Hook
#18 #19

Elizabeth-Town

SOMERSET CO. #12

#2 #20
Bonham Town
#1
Landing #3
#4 Brunswick
Perth Amboy
#11

#10
Middle Town

MIDDLESEX
CO.
#13

#9
Freehold

Crosswick
#8
Allens Town

Black Horse
#7

MONMOUTH
CO.
#14

Mount Holly

Philadelphia
#5
#6
Penny Hill
Haddonfield

N

INDEX MAP

"A Collection of Plan's
...in... New Jersey, by
Iohn Hills"
ca. 1781

0   10   20
         Miles

#15 is northern N.J.

#16

DELAWARE BAY

JPS

85

copy of this large map was rediscovered a few years ago with other old maps in an obscure corner of one of the state's warehouses.[46]

John Hills had been an active military mapper for the British General Sir Henry Clinton during the Revolution, preparing not only battle layouts but also some careful road surveys and neatly drawn regional maps. Soon after 1781 he assembled twenty of his maps—half of them based on surveys of others—into an atlas bought at auction by the Library of Congress a century later. The set, entitled *A Collection of Plan's &c. &c. &c. in the Province of New Jersey, by Iohn Hills Asst. Engr.,* is complete with title page and table of contents. Seven town plans or sketches range in subject from Paulus Hook to Haddonfield, and six road maps show routes near Mount Holly, Freehold, Paulus Hook, and Elizabethtown. Regional maps include separate mile/inch maps of Somerset, Middlesex and Monmouth (then including Ocean) Counties, as well as larger areas. The libraries of Rutgers and the Morristown National Historical Park have partial and almost complete photocopies, respectively. The East Jersey Proprietors own a rare copy of Hills's 1784 map of Perth Amboy, drawn at 400 feet/inch. This one he dedicated to the mayor, James Parker.[47]

Hills's military career apparently lasted from 1781 to 1784. He somehow was able to reconcile his Tory status with the victorious colonists. How he did, we do not know, but he soon advertised as a surveyor and draftsman. Concerning a map of New Jersey, he advertised to the "Publick" in the *New Jersey Gazette,* Oct. 11, 1784, that "I shall esteem it as a particular favour, if any gentleman travelling through Princeton will call on Mr. Hills, at the post office, to point out any error that he may be liable to make in his map."

In 1786, Hills advertised his services in a Philadelphia paper and was listed in a Philadelphia directory as a surveyor from 1794 to 1817. In 1797 and in 1808 he published outstanding large-scale maps of the Philadelphia area—the latter authorized by the U.S. House of Representatives.[48]

Although Christopher Colles was not to succeed commercially, others did. The market for American-made atlases remained untapped for only a little more than a decade. In 1795 a moderate-sized (8 miles/inch) map of New Jersey appeared in a book of maps accompanying Mathew Carey's *American Edition of Guthrie's Geography improved.* An improvement over Faden's map in accuracy,

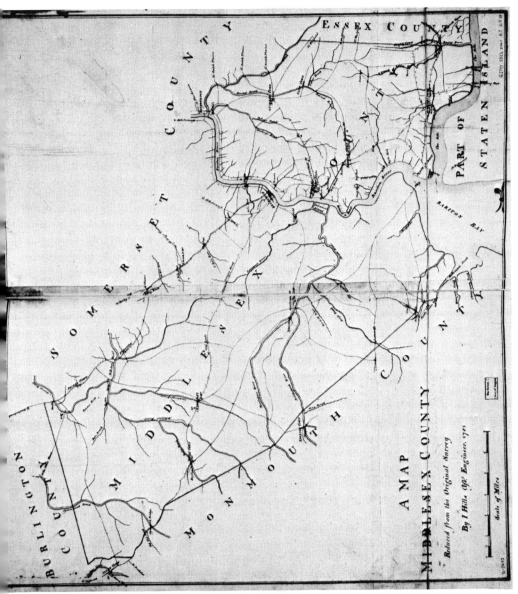

"A Survey of Middlesex County." By John Hills, ca. 1785. Map No. 13 of his "A Collection of Plan's &c. . . ." Based on surveys by Azariah Dunham and Joseph Rue, it appeared at a scale of 1 mile/inch (reduced here). *Geography and Map Division, Library of Congress.*

The State of New Jersey Compiled from the Most Authentic Information. By Samuel Lewis, 1795. Included in Mathew Carey's "American Edition of Guthrie's Geography improved," it was part of the first American-made atlas. *Rutgers University Library.*

and showing counties and several double-lined roads, it was compiled by Samuel Lewis and was revised several times into the second decade of the nineteenth century. Published in Philadelphia, it was part of the first world atlas to be engraved and published in this country.[49]

The second American map of the state was published in 1795 in Joseph T. Scott's *The United States Gazetteer*. Another Philadelphia printing, it roughly outlines counties and includes a few roads at 16 miles/inch, but it is badly foreshortened from north to south.[50] Another small Jersey map, without county lines, but also inspired by Faden, was a part of Carey's 1796 *American Pocket Atlas*, which contained a brief description of each state.

The young state, as a political entity or as a link between two large cities, was getting its share of maps. What it still lacked was the comprehensive survey necessary for maps which were fully dependable.

CHAPTER THREE

From an Art to a Science: Mapping, 1800–1888

TURNPIKES TO IRON RAILS

The growing travel and commerce of the young country led to the great toll road experiment. It did not appear practical to build the needed roads with taxes alone. Pennsylvania was the first state to charter a toll road, just as that state repeated its lead in the second wave of toll roads a century and a half later. In 1792 it was the Lancaster Turnpike, a sixty-two-mile success.

New Jersey meanwhile was developing a mining industry in Morris and Sussex Counties and required new roads for greater access to the area. The first toll road in Jersey was the Morris Turnpike, chartered in 1801 and running from Elizabeth-Town through Springfield, Morristown, Stanhope, and on to Newton. By 1829 the legislature had incorporated fifty-one turnpike companies, but only about half ever built roads. They totaled some 550 miles of "improved" highways. All were in northern or central Jersey.[1] Northwest Jersey failed to develop as quickly as expected. Sussex County, which had a greater population than any other county in the state in 1800 and 1820 (although it included Warren County at the time), became stagnant at twenty to thirty thousand for the next century, and was the least populous county in 1930 and 1950.

By 1829 several toll roads were already bankrupt. Two new kinds of competition, the canal and the railroad, crushed most of the rest, as well as numerous plank roads and turnpikes built in north and south Jersey throughout most of the nineteenth century. Surprisingly, some continued into the twentieth century. The Bergen Turnpike did not close its tollgates until 1915, after 113 years of tolls; the last toll road of the era was abandoned in 1939, when the state allowed the Pleasantville and Atlantic Turnpike or Plank Road Co. to surrender its sixty-three-year-old franchise.[2]

Two famous canals became prominent additions to maps in the early 1830's. The Morris Canal was built primarily to carry anthracite coal from Pennsylvania to New York. It could also profit from its proximity to the iron mines of Morris County. The canal was conceived by George P. McCulloch of Morristown who, while fishing on Lake Hopatcong, concluded that the lake could serve as the source of water for a stepwise channel descending to the Delaware River on the west and to the Passaic River on the east.

This was to be accomplished with a series of twenty-eight locks and twenty-three inclined planes to handle the 760-foot drop to the Delaware at Phillipsburg and the 914-foot drop to the Passaic at Newark.[3] With money and authorization secured, the ninety-mile canal was constructed along a meandering route from Newark, via Paterson, to Rockaway by 1830, and from Rockaway to Phillipsburg a year later. In 1836 a link to Jersey City was added.

The Delaware and Raritan Canal was less grandiose. Following the Delaware River, Stony Brook, the Millstone River, and the Raritan throughout most of its route from Bordentown to New Brunswick, it was completed in 1833 with fourteen locks. A feeder along the Delaware from above Lambertville was added the next year.

The D & R Canal reaped profits into the twentieth century, but the Morris Canal began failing soon after the Civil war and was abandoned in the 1920's. Some short sections still contain water, but it is now more easily traced as the route of Raymond Boulevard in Newark, of part of the Newark city subway, and of the Garden State Parkway as it passes through Bloomfield. The D & R Canal was abandoned for commerce in 1934, but still contains water under state supervision, except near Trenton, where it became the route of the Freeway.

The last survivor of all the new nineteenth-century transport routes in the area was the railroad. John Stevens of Hoboken was the first to request a railroad charter in the United States. It was

1811, and the New Jersey legislature turned him down. In 1815 he secured the charter, but failed to raise the money. In 1830, all factors were favorable; he and his sons received a charter for the Camden and Amboy Railroad, sold its stock immediately, and had completed the road from Bordentown to South Amboy by 1833.

Thus encouraged, eager investors in strong (and often vicious) competition led to a proliferation of tracks over the state, including Atlantic City in 1854. By 1885, there were over 1,900 miles of tracks, and only 158 miles of canals.[4] The railroads, and not the highways, became the standard for linking towns on the conventional maps of the late nineteenth century.

A TRAVELER'S GUIDE BY MATHEW CAREY

As the nineteenth century dawned, the strip-type road map continued to appeal to some map makers. Conceived in England and transplanted to American soil by Christopher Colles, the strip map next appeared when Mathew Carey (1760–1839), a prolific publisher and writer, prepared the second American road atlas. In a negative tribute to the limited sales of the Colles book—issued only a few years earlier—Carey's preface said "repeated demands for an American Book of Roads by native as well as foreign Travellers, have induced me to publish this Directory." [5]

Like Colles, Carey chose the most heavily traveled route, the road from New York to Washington. While not extending his atlas beyond this area as Colles did, Carey employed better-skilled engravers, and added descriptive material, entitling the whole *The Traveller's Directory: or, A Pocket Companion, shewing the Course of the Main Road from Philadelphia to New York; and from Philadelphia to Washington: with Descriptions of the Places through which It passes, and the Intersections of the Cross Roads. . . .* The two editions were printed in Philadelphia in 1802 and 1804, respectively. He shows only one route through New Jersey, essentially the same as the northerly route on Colles's maps—from Paulus Hook to Trenton, but at a smaller scale of 1 mile/inch.[6]

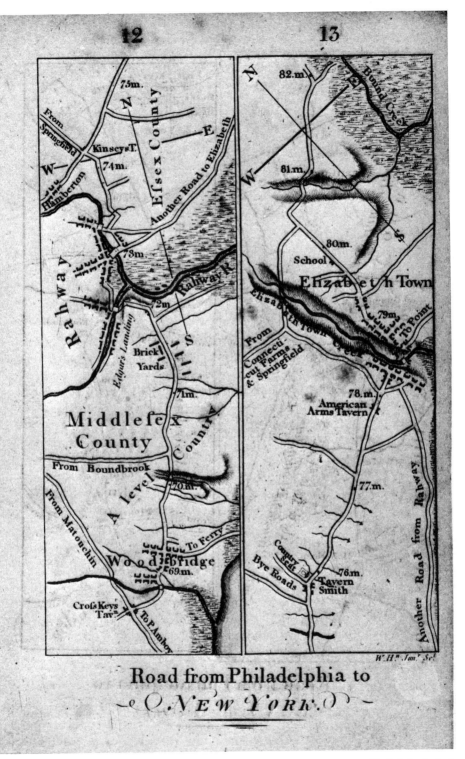

Strips 12 and 13 of Mathew Carey's "Road from Philadelphia to New York," included in his 1804 edition of *The Traveller's Directory*. The second American road atlas, this was the first to be financially successful. *Princeton University Library.*

THOMAS GORDON GIVES JERSEY
AN OFFICIAL MAP

Aside from the few road maps and composite maps of portions of the state, New Jersey desperately needed detailed, accurate maps of the entire state. In 1812, for example, William Watson of Gloucester County prepared a large map of the state, outlined in color and at a scale of 4 miles/inch, inscribed "To His Excellency Joseph Bloomfield, Governor, the Council and Assembly." It is the earliest known map to show townships for the entire state. Watson included an authoritative-looking six-inch engraving of the state shield, but he drew township lines and roads with little evidence of making more than off-hand assumptions in many cases. Some of the northern townships such as Hanover and Harrington are even shown miles away from their correct locations relative to neighbors. Watson apparently used Faden's shore and river lines as his base, improving only slightly on his county boundaries.[7]

The need for a better map had prompted the state legislature to pass an act in 1799 establishing a corporation called "The Company for procuring an accurate map of the State of New-Jersey," interestingly composed of Governor Richard Howell, William Coxe, Jr., Joshua Ladd Howell, and others. They were to have exclusive rights of sale for fifteen years, provided they sold all their stock and published a map by 1803.[8]

Apparently nothing came of this attempt. In 1822, the legislature tried again. This time they authorized a loan of $1,000 to Thomas Gordon, "the better to enable him to procure additional surveys" and defray other mapping costs, provided he repay them in two years, without interest.[9]

This time the result was monumental. In 1828, Gordon produced a high quality *A Map of the State of New Jersey* at a scale of 3 miles/inch. H. S. Tanner was the engraver. All townships are shown with considerable care. The emerging turnpike system is given distinctive marking. With half-inch-wide traces, counties are bordered in red, green, orange, or yellow. Township borders received narrow strips of color, different for adjacent townships. Gordon shows far more roads than Watson. While the Lawrence line is omitted, there

Detail from William Watson's 1812 map of New Jersey. A large map with many in-accuracies, such as the miles-off locations of Hanover and Harrington Townships. *Rutgers University Library.*

is a road shown along its path from the settlement of Westecunk (West Creek) near Little Egg Harbor to Prospertown, at the Lahaway River. Detailed roads, but no townships, are shown in counties of the neighboring states. Even Gordon's printing surpasses Watson's.[10]

New Jersey mapping had achieved a new high. Though involving some additional fieldwork, the map relied heavily on the best of existing surveys. Errors in position amounted to only three-fourths of a mile in latitude and five-eighths of a mile in longitude, according to the State Geologist sixty years later.[11]

The state legislature was pleased. It passed a resolution in March 1828 to buy 125 copies for state offices and officials, for colleges and for counties. In 1831, the state treasurer was authorized to cancel the bond and order 125 more copies, one for each township. This led to a map revision dated 1833, followed by a third edition of 1850, for which the state paid another $1,000.[12] With a last revision by Robert E. Hornor in 1854, the Gordon map stood out as the one authority for thirty years.

Thomas Gordon was born in 1778 at Amwell, soon moving to Trenton, where he spent most of his life. He was not only a surveyor, but also a judge of the Court of Common Pleas. Although he was appointed librarian of the young New Jersey Historical Society in 1845 and 1846, he was inactive due to his health. In 1848 he died in Trenton, where he was buried.[13]

Like many others with common names, he was confused with a namesake. Thomas Francis Gordon, born in Philadelphia in 1787, actually became more famous to later history enthusiasts than did the surveyor. What compounded the confusion was the fact that both sold maps, and both were avid students of history and law.

While the elder Gordon was producing his large map, the younger Gordon was busy compiling gazetteers and histories of the three Middle Atlantic states. His *History of Pennsylvania* appeared in 1829, *History of America* in 1831, and *Gazetteer of the State of Pennsylvania* in 1832. He wrote a history of Mexico, and issued digests of federal and Pennsylvania laws. For Jerseyans, however, his most famous work is his *Gazetteer of the State of New Jersey* and *History of New Jersey*, published together and separately in 1834. Daniel Fenton of Trenton was the publisher.

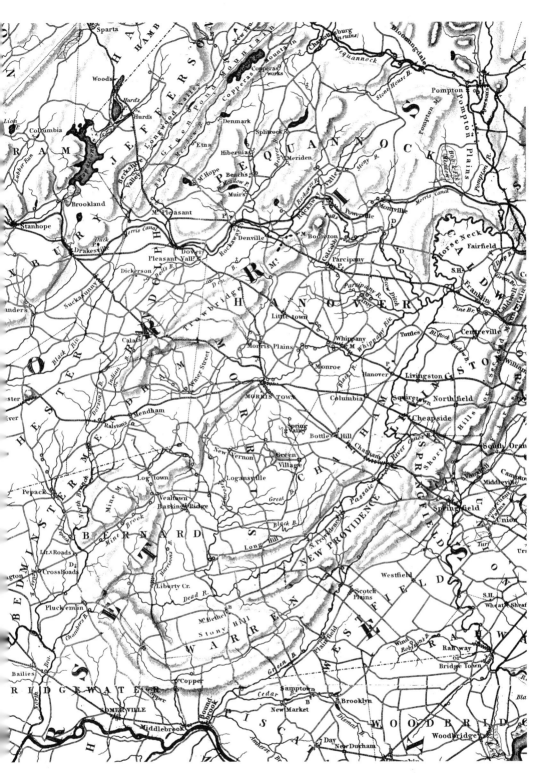

Detail from *A Map of the State of New Jersey*. By Thomas Gordon, 1828. By far the most accurate map to date. At 3 miles/inch, the map was subsidized by the state, and ran to four editions over twenty-six years. This detail is reduced in scale. *Rutgers University Library*.

Widely distributed, the *Gazetteer* lists nearly every named river, community, mountain, township, and county in the state. A paragraph or several pages for each town lists the number of dwellings, churches, taverns, mills, and other features which help to recreate the town in the minds of nostalgic local history enthusiasts. For example, this description is typical for postage-stamp communities still on today's maps:

"*Jacobstown*, Hanover t-ship, Burlington co., near the Great Monmouth Road, 12 miles N. E. from Mount Holly, and 9 miles S. E. of Bordentown; contains 2 taverns, a store, and some 12 or 15 dwellings." [14]

With the *Gazetteer*, T. F. Gordon included a small hand-colored map of New Jersey (published by A. Finley of Philadelphia) emphasizing, at last, railroads and canals against the random crossing of major roads. With the help of the other Gordon's 1828 map, he could produce a high degree of accuracy in a map of this size. Almost in tribute to the dying practice of including ornamental cartouches, the title "New Jersey" is surrounded only by a dense cloud.

It is not clear whether the older Thomas Gordon considered T. F. G. to have ambitions beyond his capabilities, but he clearly became irked by the confusion of names, so much so that he placed an advertisement:

TO THE PUBLIC: Understanding that owing to the similitude of names, an impression has prevailed that *I* was the author of that History and Gazeteer of N.J. and that the Map to accompany the work (as actually promised in the prospectus) was to be reduced from my Map of N.J.; this Book with a Map accompanying (such as they are) being now published, and lest a further silence on my part might be deemed a connivance or imposition upon the public, I think proper to make it distinctly known that I am not the author of the work; but that Thomas F. Gordon of Philadelphia, is the author of the book and that the Map accompanying it was neither prepared by me, nor with my permission for that publication. May 5, 1834. Editors in this state are requested to publish the above. Thomas Gordon, of N.J. [15]

The son of a Scottish immigrant, Thomas F. Gordon married a girl whose early life involved a series of romantic tragedies. Her father, born in France, had moved to Santo Domingo (in the present-day Dominican Republic), where his wife gave birth to their two children. The night before a slave uprising, he had fled the island for the United States, on the advice of a "faithful servant," and had settled in Philadelphia. He then called for the rest of his family, who had previously been sent back to France. On their voyage to join him, they were shipwrecked off the Spanish coast. His wife and one child drowned in the surf when their lifeboat capsized, but little Constance, lashed to the back of the nurse, survived when the nurse swam to shore. Constance lived to marry Thomas F. Gordon and to bear eight children.

Studying archeology and history, Gordon was admitted to the Pennsylvania bar in 1806 and was later clerk of the Orphans' Court. In his later years he became very deaf, and died in Beverly, N.J., in January of 1860.[16]

The advent of the elder Gordon's high-caliber map of 1828 did not assure equal or superior accuracy in all later ones. John T. Hammond in 1835 prepared a "Wilcox's Map" of the state (with counties, but not townships) at 6⅔ miles/inch. At less than half the scale of Gordon's 1828 map, it did not meet Gordon's standards. Hammond did incorporate street maps of five cities into insets on this map, and on another edition of 1836, called "Squire's Map." On a similar "Distance Map" of 1845, he marked mileages on the various roads. Counties were separately hand-colored. (Hand-coloring was often risky: on Rutgers' copy of this map, half of Morris County was painted into Passaic County!) [17]

THE U.S. COAST SURVEY BEGINS IN NEW JERSEY: FERDINAND HASSLER

Two decades after the establishment of the Public Land Survey under Thomas Hutchins, Congress turned its attention to another phase of mapping. In 1807, it authorized the President to "cause a survey to be taken of coasts of the United States." Ferdinand Rudolph Hassler was promptly hired to head the bureau, first called Survey of the Coast.

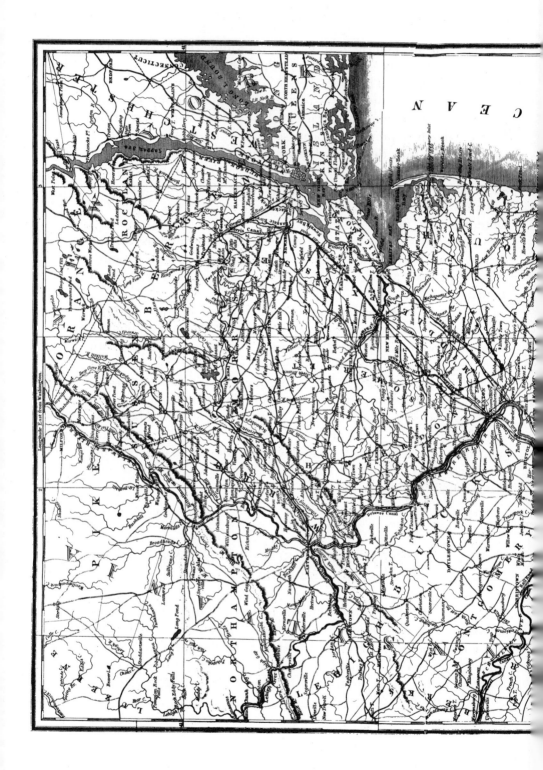

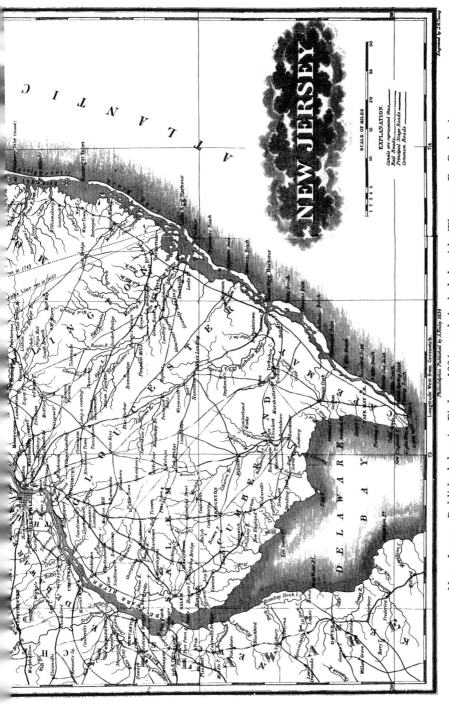

New Jersey. Published by A. Finley, 1834, and included with Thomas F. Gordon's *Gazetteer*. With fourteen counties, it shows the Morris and Delaware & Raritan Canals and the earliest railroads as the railroad boom began. This Gordon was not the same as the author of the 1828 map. *Rutgers University Library.*

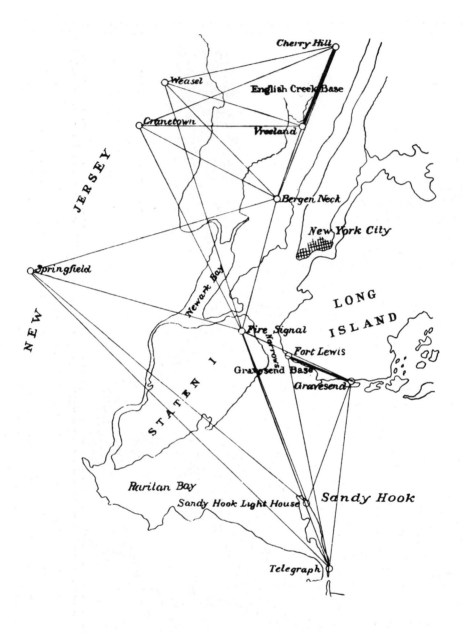

Triangulation network of the first U.S. Coast Survey, 1817. Supervised by Ferdinand Hassler, one of the base lines was in northeast New Jersey. *Rutgers University Library.*

Ferdinand Rudolph Hassler (1770–1843), first Superintendent of the U.S. Coast Survey. He led some of its earliest work in New Jersey. *Rutgers University Library.*

Born in Switzerland in 1770, Hassler arrived in the United States in 1805. After his appointment, he was forced to wait four years for funds and equipment, meanwhile teaching to maintain income. When funds were granted in 1811, he left for Europe to obtain the necessary equipment, not returning until 1815.

Geodetic surveying began at last in 1816 with two base lines, each about four miles long. One ran almost north and south just west of Englewood, N.J. The other ran west from Gravesend, Long Island. By the next year Hassler had developed a small triangulation network extending to Springfield, N.J., and Telegraph Hill in Monmouth County. Triangulation, a German invention of the sixteenth century,[18] consists of establishing a network of points whose location with respect to neighboring points is precisely known by distance and direction.

Congress was not impressed with the progress and in 1818 transferred the Survey from the Treasury Department to the Navy, excluding Hassler and civilian employees. The Survey almost stopped functioning until its return to Treasury in 1832 with Hassler as superintendent. Shuttled back and forth once again—but retaining Hassler—it became the Coast Survey in 1836.

The Survey's first maps (1834) involved New York and Long Island. The earliest nautical chart depicted Newark Bay in 1839. There was little detail, but the accuracy was high. Hassler spent the fall of 1843 in the field making geodetic surveys in New Jersey and Delaware. In Delaware he was caught in a severe wind- and hailstorm that swept away tents protecting his instruments. Trying to save the instruments, the superintendent fell on a rock, injuring himself and remaining exposed to the weather for several hours. Never recovering, he died in Philadelphia in November 1843. Hassler was noted for stubbornness, perseverance, intolerance, and technical excellence which won and lost supporters, but firmly established the Coast Survey. In 1878 it was renamed the Coast and Geodetic Survey, and in 1903 it became part of the Department of Commerce.[19] The Survey was consolidated with another agency in 1965, but five years later, in a general reorganization, that agency was abolished, and the survey work was assumed by the newly formed National Ocean Survey.

NEW JERSEY'S GEOLOGICAL SURVEY IS BORN: ROGERS AND KITCHELL

The extensive geological resources under the ground beckoned to the state for a careful study of their potential. It was this need that led finally to the development of highly accurate maps. Henry D. Rogers (1808–1866) was appointed the first New Jersey state geologist in 1835. Simultaneously serving as state geologist of Pennsylvania and professor at the University of Pennsylvania, he proceeded to make a geological survey of New Jersey between 1836 and 1840, using Gordon's map as the base.[20]

Work was halted—unfunded—for fourteen years, until the state in 1854 appointed Dr. William Kitchell state geologist and superintendent of the new New Jersey Geological Survey.[21] Kitchell, born near Bottle Hill (now Madison) in 1827, began his college training at Rutgers. After two years he changed to medicine. He taught at the Newark Institute but did not set up practice. About 1850, he left this field as well and traveled to Europe for study at the Mining School of Freiberg, Germany. Thus he qualified for the post of state geologist, and immediately launched a more complete survey of New Jersey.

Kitchell's staff of three included a new professor at Rutgers named George H. Cook as his assistant in charge of surveying the "Southern Division" of the state. Kitchell supervised the Northern Division. A chemist, Dr. Henry Wurtz, and a topographic engineer, General Egbert L. Viele, completed the staff.

The topographic survey was confidently begun in Sussex County, the heart of the mineral lands, in 1854, with plane tables and triangulation. By the next year, Sussex and Cape May surveys were considered complete and maps drawn, with several other counties under way. The legislature was not convinced of the need and stopped the funding after only two years. When work was halted in 1856, Monmouth was the only other county completed, and Viele showed obvious disappointment as he remarked, for example, that Morris "could have been completed in about three weeks." [22]

The State Agricultural Society, regretting the loss of the interrupted work, in 1860 persuaded the legislature to let Kitchell complete the geological survey. He was allowed to use the maps and apparatus already on hand, provided he do so at his own expense and return the state's property afterward. The 1860 law also demanded copies of a new map of the state to be prepared at a scale no smaller than 3 miles/inch. [23]

Thus New Jersey arrived at the next milestone in its mapping, although the map was privately published. Based on the geological survey to date, and also on information from the U.S. Coast Survey, Kitchell and George M. Hopkins, a civil engineer, prepared a new high-quality, detailed map of New Jersey in 1860 at a scale of 2½ miles/inch. The publisher was H. G. Bond of Philadelphia.

County boundaries are bordered in red; each township received a solid tint of pink, yellow, orange or green. The cartographers attempted to show every street with fine double lines. Seventeen colored insets give detailed street maps of towns ranging in size from Newark to Mount Holly. A meteorological map of New Jersey

Reduced detail from the beautiful map of New Jersey prepared in 1860 by William Kitchell and George M. Hopkins. Based on state and federal surveys, it was privately published by H. G. Bond at 2½ miles/inch, and was the next landmark after Gordon's 1828 map. *Rutgers University Library.*

comprises another inset, and there are panoramic views—black and white engravings—of five cities and the Delaware Water Gap.

One unique addition and sign of the times before standard time zones is a "Time Dial showing the time at the several County Seats when it is 12 o'clock at the Capitol." Newark's time was declared to be 12h 02m 24s, while Salem clocks would read 11h 57m 30s. The road following the southern part of the Lawrence line, shown by Gordon, no longer appears, but the dotted Lawrence line is back, shown only at its extremities in Ocean and Sussex Counties.[24]

Kitchell did not complete his survey. He died suddenly of "some acute disease" in 1861, at the age of thirty-four. His death led the Agricultural Society to obtain another law, in 1863, to shift the completion of the work to George Cook, "or some other suitable person."[25]

A SPOTLIGHT ON COUNTY MAPS

Incomplete as it was, the Kitchell survey and his attractive map prompted several other cartographers to prepare detailed atlas maps of the state. Beginning in 1868, G. W. & C. B. Colton & Co., who had brought out small maps of the state for over a decade, issued a new map, frequently to be revised, at a scale of 7½ miles/inch. It shows detailed roads, and each township is separately colored. (In 1879, they produced a *Larger Township Map . . .* at 5 miles/ inch.)[26] Similar maps at 8 miles/inch, with or without roads, were prepared by H. H. Lloyd and also A. J. Johnson, both of New York.[27]

G. M. Hopkins, Kitchell's associate on the 1860 map, and State Topographer under Cook in the mid-1860's, published a state map of his own at 4 miles/inch in 1872. He obtained financing in the large northern towns from dozens of merchants, whose neatly printed calling-card-type ads decorate the edges of his map.[28]

Large scale single- or multisheet commercial maps of counties were also blossoming forth from publishers as numerous as the counties. Although Thomas Gordon had produced a map of Warren County in 1825 at the modest scale of 4 miles/inch, the county maps did not generally begin to appear until 1849, with a map of Burling-

Burlington County, detail. From "Original Surveys by J. W. Otley & R. Whiteford,"
1849. The first of an extensive series of large scale county sheet maps, most of them
identifying property owners. *Rutgers University Library*.

ton County at about 0.8 mile/inch, prepared by J. W. Otley and R. Whiteford and published by Smith & Wistar of Philadelphia. Hunterdon, Morris, Camden, Sussex, and others were represented by 1860 at a scale of 1½ inches/mile, although from a variety of authors. Property owners were identified on many. Unlike its role in the development of commercial county street maps a century later, the population of a county seemed to have little effect upon its suitability as the subject of a large map. By 1872, all but four counties were in print at the 1½ inches/mile scale or larger.

A nationally popular endeavor, especially in the northeastern states, Texas and California, the field of county map making attracted many a civil engineer with a commercial bent. Hopkins helped to prepare maps or atlases of four Jersey counties, but Henry Francis Walling (1825–1888) was one of the most prolific and skillful nationally. Entering the field with a cadastral (land ownership) map of a Massachusetts town in 1848, and of Newport County, R.I., in 1850, he moved his offices from Providence to Boston to produce maps of 280 counties (including four in New Jersey), over twenty states and provinces, and a hundred cities and "special localities." Following the Civil war, he briefly concentrated on the publication of state atlases, but spent the last eighteen years of his life employed by the U.S. Coast and Geodetic Survey and the U.S. Geological Survey.[29]

At about the same time, atlases of New Jersey and its counties were appearing for the first time. Before long there was a substantial group of county atlases showing towns, streets, and the names of landowners in neatly drafted, colored books. Again, no one map maker controlled the field. F. W. Beers issued atlases of Morris County in 1868, Somerset, Middlesex, Monmouth, and Hunterdon in 1873, and Warren the next year. Everts & Stewart published atlases of Mercer, Middlesex, Salem, and Gloucester in 1875–6. Elisha Robinson produced Union, Morris, and Essex County atlases during the 1880's. With others offering single entries, by 1890 fifteen of the counties were covered by commercial atlases. Some counties never had their own popular atlases, and revisions of general atlases for others stopped early in the twentieth century.[30] The county sheet-maps and atlases of that period are listed in the Appendix.

Special-purpose county atlases, for setting fire insurance rates, or to delineate property owners, reached a more restricted market. The

Sanborn Map Co. and Franklin Survey led these fields in the early 1900's.

Of special interest in 1872 was the first atlas to show each part of New Jersey in detail. It is entitled *State Atlas of New Jersey, based on State Geological Survey and from additional Surveys,* by F. W. Beers. It was published in New York City, engraved on stone. It contains a map of each county (or in some cases two or three in a group) at a scale of 2 miles/inch, as well as a geological map and a state map divided into municipalities at 8 miles/inch. Over fifty towns and cities are further enlarged at varying scales, naming streets and, in some cases, property owners.

Beers's *State Atlas* maps are neatly printed and somewhat crudely colored, with minor errors in some boundaries, but they combine to present a proliferation of details about New Jersey roads, railroads, and canals of the post-Civil war era. Labeled "topographical maps," they lack contours and woodland designations, but otherwise present the amount of detail shown in modern government topographical maps of a similar scale.

In 1873, Hopkins published his *Combined Atlas of New Jersey and the City of Newark,* and a similar *Combined Atlas of New Jersey and the County of Hudson.* Except for Essex, Union, and Hudson, his county maps are only shown at 4 miles/inch, a smaller scale than his map of 1860. The other three counties appear at 2 miles/inch, but most of each atlas is devoted to large-scale maps of all sections of Newark (or Hudson County). The style of the county maps is similar to Beers's, and similar problems appear in the coloring and in a few boundaries, such as the Monmouth-Ocean County boundary, which was erroneously shown along the Metedeconk River, eventually correct, but fifty-five years early!

Only one other New Jersey state atlas has been produced commercially. The high quality of its drafting in some ways surpasses Beers's atlas. It could also be more accurate, since it was issued after the great topographic survey. Published in 1905 by the Survey Map Co. of New York City, the *Atlas of the State of New Jersey* shows each county on a separate pair of facing pages. Municipalities are separately colored. The county map scales vary from 1¾ inches/mile for Hudson to ½ inch/mile for Cumberland and Morris. All streets are finely shown, but only the main ones are named, except

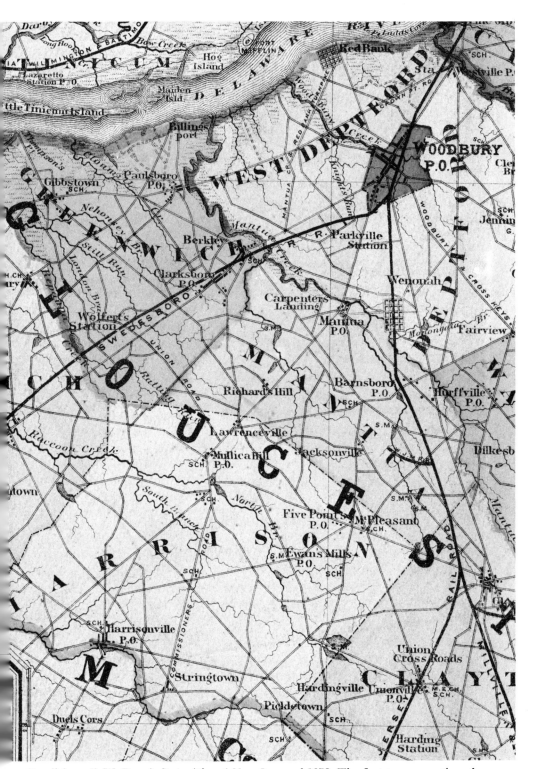

Detail from F. W. Beers's *State Atlas of New Jersey* of 1872. The first to appear, the atlas showed counties at 2 miles/inch. Beers's maps were called "topographical," but this term was later applied only to maps showing contour lines as well. *Rutgers University Library.*

on the numerous enlarged street maps of principal towns. Even the houses in rural areas are marked with dots.

PROFESSOR COOK COMPLETES A SURVEY

The maps of the 1860's and 1870's still lacked the benefit of the detailed topographic survey which was yet to come. Its final impetus began with a law of March 1864, when the state legislature passed "An act to complete the geological survey of the state." In the act, it was declared that George H. Cook was to be appointed the third state geologist. This was a fortunate choice.

George Hammell Cook was born in Hanover, Morris County, in 1818. At eighteen he helped survey the route for the Morris and Essex Railroad, which was to run from Newark to Morristown and beyond. Two years later he began to study geology at Rensselaer Polytechnic Institute at Troy, N.Y. He taught there after graduation the next year, and by 1846, when he married, he was a senior professor. He later taught at a nearby academy, where he was principal when he left in 1853 for Rutgers College. There he spent the rest of his life.

The state of New York had sent him to Europe to study salt deposits on behalf of the salt industry of Onondaga County, N.Y. This gave him one more credential to merit his appointment as professor of chemistry and natural sciences at Rutgers when he arrived, and to qualify him for the post as Kitchell's assistant state geologist from 1854 to 1856.

Perhaps his role as state geologist from March 1864 until his sudden death in September 1889 brought him the most fame, but he was equally outstanding for his role in establishing the College of Agriculture at Rutgers. This dual role was symbolic of the output of a man noted for his tremendous energy and perseverance. In building up the school's collection of geological and scientific specimens, for example, he would first ask for appealing specimens to be donated. Failing this, he sought funds from almost any source. On numerous occasions, he would finally pay for the specimens himself—revealing the solution to his problem only upon the most intensive interrogation by his associates.

As the dynamic proponent of the agricultural college, Cook's down-to-earth approach of chatting with and learning endlessly from New Jersey farmers themselves earned him broad support, and earned Rutgers the school, established under the Morrill Act of 1862. Cook had received his Ph.D. from New York University in 1856 and was made a vice-president of Rutgers the year he became state geologist. Three years later he also began teaching the theory and practice of agriculture.

Cook toured Europe twice during the 1870's to study agricultural techniques, and in 1881 persuaded the state to grant $5,000 for an agricultural experiment station. Made director of the station, he immediately asked the state to reduce his salary as state geologist by the $1,000 he received as director.[31] During his last six years he

George Hammell Cook (1818–1889). State Geologist from 1864 until his death, his perseverance led to the complete topographic survey of the state. He also launched the Agricultural College of Rutgers in 1862, and founded the Agricultural Experiment Station in 1881. *Rutgers University Library.*

was also surveyor general for the East Jersey Proprietors. While in the post, he was drawn into some questionable land purchases dominated by the register of the Proprietors. In an 1896 court decision (after the death of both men), the Proprietors were awarded a moderate sum from the register's estate, but Cook's action was only mildly criticized.[32]

As required by the enabling acts, Cook issued annual reports as state geologist, and they were far from perfunctory. From these reports, especially in 1885 and 1888, a detailed picture of the development of the first complete topographic survey of any state in the nation can be drawn.

The 1864 law granted Cook only four years and $20,000. With Hopkins as cartographer, a 900-page report with a four-section geological map of the state at a scale of 2 miles/inch was produced in 1868, only a few months late. Using the information developed under Kitchell, the Survey added data from various county and local maps and surveys.[33]

All municipalities on the map are bordered in color. All streets are shown, but not labeled, and dots represent houses in some but not all the outlying areas. Its main geological role does not submerge its usefulness as a cultural and political map, since the rock formations in solid color are few enough and light enough to make the base map quite legible.[34] As with earlier landmark maps, neatness in drafting did not assure accuracy of locations. To those in charge, the map and report only helped point up again what was still needed.

As Cook reported later, at first a topographic survey was not considered, but he soon began to see that

for the study and preparation of useful geological reports it was necessary to have accurate maps—maps which would show the location of all the important geographical points, and also the outlines and elevations of the hills and valleys, and their heights above the sea level. There were no such maps of New Jersey in existence, nor, indeed, of any others of the United States.[35]

To put it bluntly, existing maps of New Jersey were "unreliable and insufficient . . . simply because no actual survey has ever been made. Originally compiled from disconnected, inharmonious and largely unreliable sources, they have been copied and recopied." [36]

The only consolation was that maps of the other states were even worse.

Fortunately, Cook reported, the need met with popular and legislative approval (undoubtedly thanks to his persuasive abilities). At four- or five-year intervals the legislature granted further time and money ($5,000 per year at first; $8,000 in the grant of 1876), resulting in the welcome fact that the New Jersey Geological Survey has remained continuously funded from 1864 to the present. It is now called the Bureau of Geology and Topography.

When New Jersey's northern boundary line was resurveyed in 1874, the shocking fact emerged that a line considered straight—based on the 1774 survey—was actually a wandering line a half mile out in its center. It was the victim of the Highlands' magnetic iron ore, which upset the surveyors' magnetic compasses. This gave further impetus to the need for the triangulation which Congress in 1871 had authorized the U.S. Coast Survey (shortly to become the U.S. Coast and Geodetic Survey) to furnish to each state which would provide for its own geological survey. So it came about that Cook could happily report in 1888, in his final report as state geologist, only a year before he died, that a topographic survey of the entire state had been completed.[37]

The Coast Survey supplied most of the triangulation, latitudes, and longitudes as part of their assigned work. The new U.S. Geological Survey, formed in 1879, funded and administered the last half of the Topographic Survey, starting in 1884, and thereby shared in all the information obtained.

C. C. VERMEULE AND THE FIRST CONTOUR MAPS OF A STATE

The guiding light in the fieldwork of the surveys was Cornelius Clarkson Vermeule, a civil engineer then in his twenties, who conducted all of them, both state and federally funded, from 1879 to 1888, and who wrote much of Cook's final report.[38]

This position as topographer was only the beginning of a long career of outstanding engineering for Vermeule. Born in New Brunswick, N.J., in 1858, he was descended from Adrian Vermeule,

Cornelius Clarkson Vermeule (1858–1950), civil engineer in charge of the first topographic survey of an American state—that of New Jersey. After completing the survey in 1888, he continued as a consulting engineer for fifty-five years. *Rutgers University Library.*

who was one of the early Dutch settlers of the village of Bergen, dating to 1700. The surveyor was graduated from Rutgers College in 1878 with a bachelor's degree, in 1880 with a degree of civil engineer, and the next year with a master's degree. In 1888, the year he completed his ten years as topographer with the New Jersey Geological Survey, he married a New York colonel's daughter (who was to bear him two sons) and became a consulting engineer to the Geological Survey and the state. These consulting duties lasted thirty years and included the design of concrete jetties for the regulation of Shark River Inlet, and the preparation in 1894 of a report on the development of New Jersey's water supply.

Simultaneously, he opened civil engineering consulting offices in New York, continuing his practice until retiring in 1943. His clients, private corporations and governments alike, embraced over a hundred municipalities across the country, including East Orange,

N.J., and several others for whom he designed water supply systems.

In 1901, he received first prize from the Newark Board of Trade for the best plan of reclaiming the Newark Meadows.[39] In 1924 he was the consulting engineer for the New Jersey legislature in their decision to abandon the century-old Morris Canal. He was responsible for the water supply at the Duke estate near Somerville. He engineered and installed dams in northern Jersey; he designed waterworks and a power plant in Cuba. His long, productive life ended in the town of his birth, Feb. 1, 1950, at the age of 91.[40] His descendants remember him as kind and conscientious.[41]

The geodetic surveying technique employed by the Geological Survey field crews involved several basic phases. First, as with the Coast Survey in 1817, a triangulation grid was necessary. The triangulation was begun in June 1875 from Mount Rose (near Princeton) and Newtown, Pa., where locations were accurately known from work of the Coast Survey.[42]

The goal was to set points from five to twenty miles apart. Where heavily wooded, level areas were involved, it was sometimes necessary to erect scaffolds and tripods forty feet high. This was done on Mount Rose and on another hill in the summer of 1876 to support the observer and his theodolite (similar to a surveyor's transit, but more refined and a great deal more accurate) so that he could cover a greater distance. In most cases, however, church spires, house roofs, and the like served nicely for elevated perches, as the surveyor took sites on several landmarks with a repeating theodolite containing a large telescope. Repeated measurements of the same point were taken to assure a high standard of accuracy. Bad weather could be a serious problem, and it was reported that "Days are frequently spent without a single satisfactory observation, sometimes whole weeks together." [43]

By 1883 north Jersey was triangulated, and, four years later, so was south Jersey. The 457 points whose latitude and longitude were established by this technique were declared to be located with an error of less than one inch per mile.[44]

Meanwhile, the roads were being surveyed with compass and odometer, or perambulator, to provide reference lines for the topographer in locating his level stations and in sketching topography. Equipped with level, compass, protractor, scale, road sketch, and (in very hilly areas) an aneroid barometer and clinometer, the topog-

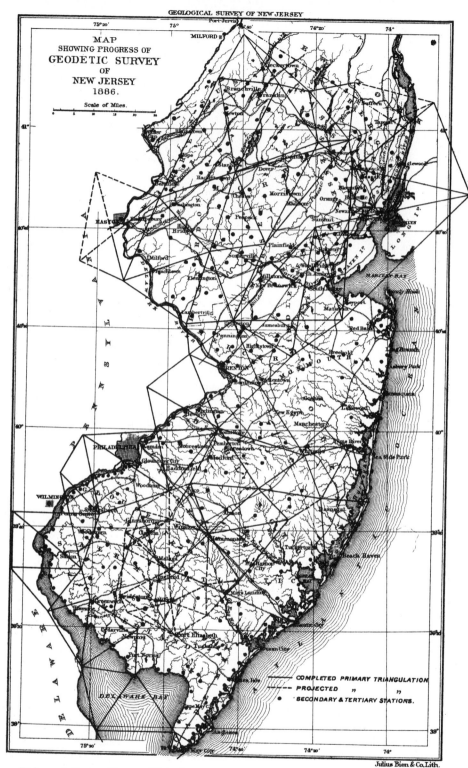

Triangulation grid over New Jersey as shown in the State Geologist's Annual
Report of 1886. *Rutgers University Library.*

118

rapher proceeded to measure elevations and to sketch streams and shapes of land.[45]

Simultaneously, the Coast and Geodetic Survey ran a series of "bench marks," or monuments marked with the elevation above mean sea level at Sandy Hook. The monuments weighed a ton each and were designed to be safe from destruction by vandals or by the curious. They consisted of granite posts thirty inches tall and eight to ten inches square, of which nine inches on the top end had been ground to a cylindrical shape with a rounded end. Nine inches below the top, there was a shoulder marked with the number of the monument, the letters N.J.G.S., and the year. The monument was cemented into a hole four feet deep and two feet square, in which a glass insulating cap had first been cemented in place and usually covered with a layer of sand. If the top were damaged, there was the special shoulder just nine inches lower. If the shoulder were damaged, the glass would almost certainly remain intact at a known depth.[46]

The bench marks were independent of the triangulation grid, but they also traversed the entire state and were essential to the topographic survey.[47]

The office work, ideal for bad weather, consisted of assembling and plotting all the information. The sketches, bench marks, triangulation, and odometer work all interacted to permit checks for consistency. With the data placed on a polyconic projection base,

Sketch of the type of monument used for the bench marks of the Coast and Geodetic Survey in the 1880's, as shown in the *Annual Report of the State Geologist for the Year 1885. Rutgers University Library.*

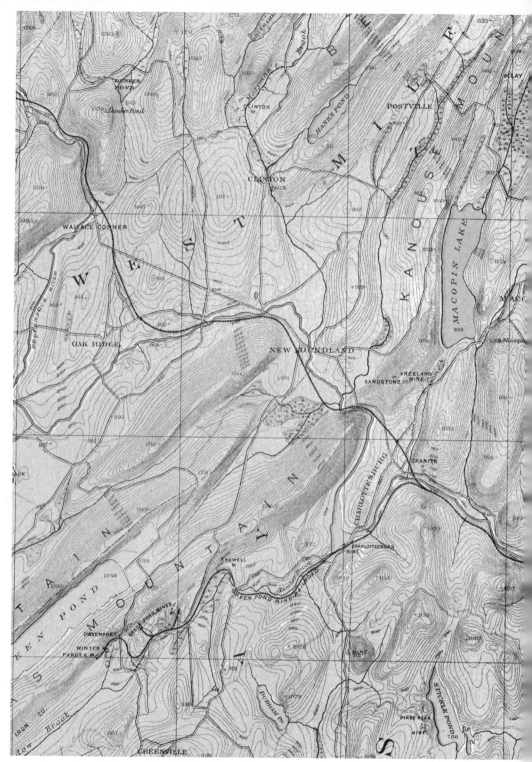

A portion of the original Atlas Sheet #3, issued by the New Jersey Geological Survey in 1884. An early product of the topographic survey. The area near Newfoundland is shown, with 20' contours, place names, all streets and occasional marked elevations. Full size. *Rutgers University Library.*

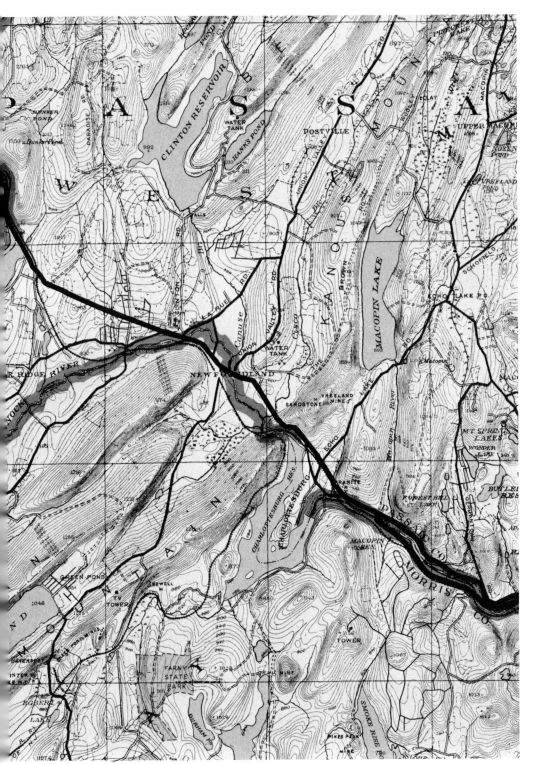

The same area shown in the preceding map, this time from the latest edition, 1960, of Atlas Sheet #22. Although culture has been updated, the old contour lines are still considered accurate. The scale of each map is 1 mi./inch. *N.J. Bureau of Geology and Topography.*

contour lines and culture could be filled in. This projection will be described later.

The cost of all this work was just under $55,000 for fieldwork and manuscript preparation. Involved in this modest fee were 18,000 man-days, 14,600 miles of levels, 18,800 miles of odometer traverse, 956 miles of transit traverse, and 215,000 odometer and transit stations.[48]

From this intensive surveying, New Jersey could have truly topographical maps. Called "Atlas Sheets" (as are their updated revisions), the maps were drawn between 1884 and 1887 on seventeen consecutively numbered sheets at a scale of 1 mile/inch. Approximately 28′ of latitude by 26′ of longitude, they overlapped neighboring sheets by amounts varying widely from almost none to one-third of the map. One area appeared on four sheets. Redrawn from manuscript drawings with three times the scale of the Atlas Sheets, they were engraved on a very fine-grained limestone [49] and issued in three colors: brown for contours, blue for water, and black for culture outlines and printing.

The seventeen first editions, the 1888 State map, and the 1889 Geological Map (Sheet 20) were bound together to form the *Atlas of New Jersey,* published by the Geological Survey and lithographed by Julius Bien & Co. of New York.

In 1903 the overlapping of the Atlas Sheets was eliminated for an edge-match system exactly 28′ of latitude by 26′ of longitude, and the resulting sheets were given the numbers 21 through 37. Sheet 37 (Cape May County) still overlapped a considerable portion of Sheets 35 and 36. Sheet 37 is being discontinued, and its unique portion made an inset on Sheet 36. In 1956 two additional colors improved the readability and made the maps much more attractive: red to emphasize major roads and green for county boundaries and parklands.

With revisions at intervals of one to twenty years, the earlier sheets are no longer available. The state will make diazo reproductions of any sheet for a price, but many of the editions are in the files of various libraries.[50] The various Atlas Sheet editions are listed in the Appendix.

From the large-scale maps, smaller-scale maps could then be prepared by the state, as additional Atlas Sheets. At a scale of 5 miles/-inch, an official map of the state was produced in 1887 as Atlas Sheet

No. 18, and various forms were issued over the next twenty years to emphasize relief, geology, forests, watersheds, municipalities, and roads, as the need arose. Since about 1910, the base map of the state has been drawn at 4 miles/inch.

At long last, accurate maps of the state could be prepared with confidence. Subsequent refinements consisted chiefly of updating and procedural details. Two hundred years of reshaping New Jersey maps had come to an end.

CHAPTER FOUR

Maps for the Millions: Mapping Since 1888

KING HIGHWAY

In the late nineteenth century railroad maps were more popular than highway maps. Railroads appeared as heavy lines on numerous maps issued not only by individual railroad companies, but also by private map makers. One of the largest railroad maps of the state was published in 1887 by John T. Van Cleef and J. Brognard Betts. At 4¼ miles/inch, it is inscribed "By authority of the State Board of Assessors of N.J." Each county is separately colored, township outlines are shown, and roads are omitted. The railroads stand out in wide black lines.[1]

Transportation supremacy began to shift from the railroad to the highway so slowly at the turn of the twentieth century that it was almost imperceptible. In 1909 the entire United States had only five miles of concrete road. Macadam, asphalt, and brick roads predominated. The responsibility for maintaining roads had rested with counties and municipalities of New Jersey until 1891, when New Jersey became the first state to subsidize local roads.[2] The municipalities previously had had little incentive to spend their money for the benefit of an outsider who was merely passing through.

Having the state subsidy was not the same as having a state highway system. The latter first appeared in 1912, when the legislature passed an "Act to establish a State system of highways." The Commissioner of Public Roads was directed to submit a state highway plan which, in 1917, resulted in another law in which fifteen numbered routes were set up. These were to be laid out "as short and

direct as practicable between the points specified." [3] Existing highways were to be used where convenient, but new highways were
quite permissible. Fifteen numbered routes were not enough: in
1920 a sixteenth was added, by 1925 there were twenty, and in 1927
the number jumped to fifty, not counting several spurs designated as
S-routes. There were both State and U.S. Routes 1, 30, 40, etc., and
various state roads coincided with portions of U.S. highways.

By the middle of the century the numbering system was so bulky
that the motorist could be thoroughly confused. It was reported
that on one pole there were listed "as many as seven U.S. and N.J.
routes." [4] There was not only State Road 25, for example. There
were S-25, 25-A, 25-AD, 25-B, 25-M, and 25-T. It is little wonder that
the State Highway Department decided to renumber most of its
highways, effective Jan. 1, 1953. All state road designations on U.S.
highways were removed, and all state route numbers which were the
same as federal numbers were abandoned.

Thus old State Route 29, running from Newark to Trenton via
Somerville and Lambertville, was abandoned as a route number between Newark and Lambertville, leaving just U.S. Routes 22 and
202. State Route 29 now runs from Frenchtown to Trenton. State
Route 1 vanished as a marker, bowing to U.S. 1. The number 25
went into oblivion altogether as a route number, state or federal.
Three digit numbers for secondary state routes completed the state
marking system. After making 543 changes on their Esso road maps,
General Drafting Co., like their competitors, rushed to get the new
marking system into the gasoline stations for the frustrated motorists. [5]

Improvement of intrastate roads, including the bypassing of several towns, was not enough. In 1921 the Port of New York Authority
was formed to improve transportation in the New York metropolitan area. Another bistate commission completed the Holland Tunnel, linking Jersey City with lower Manhattan, in 1927. It joined
the Port Authority four years later. The Goethals Bridge and Outer-
bridge Crossing to Staten Island were opened in 1928, the George
Washington Bridge from Fort Lee to Manhattan in 1931, the Pulaski
Skyway over the Passaic River and Hackensack meadows in 1932,
and the Lincoln Tunnel to midtown Manhattan in 1937. Bridge
after bridge has crossed the Delaware River, until there are now
about two dozen.

With a new New Jersey Turnpike built in 1951 (there was one a century earlier, but running from east to west), spanning the state from Ridgefield to Deepwater, the Garden State Parkway serving the east coast after 1955, and the Atlantic City Expressway by 1964, Jersey had made a serious dent in transportation tie-ups with speed toll roads, but these were being rapidly crowded.

The Interstate highway system, although plagued with money problems, began to make its mark on highway maps about 1960. With all of the numbering systems, it is more difficult to get lost while driving from one of the state to another. The problem now is driving without heavy congestion. In self-defense, the driver must often resort to the old unnumbered local roads—with a good, detailed road map—to enjoy his trip through the many fresh-air haunts in New Jersey.

COUNTIES AND TOWNS

Most Jersey road maps show the boundaries of the twenty-one counties, but there are too many municipalities for most state maps to show any local boundaries except for the larger towns. There is some doubt that most motorists really care when they cross even a county line.

Some road and atlas map makers have already discarded the county lines, or they make them so light that they are hardly visible, but in New Jersey, at least, most residents are quite conscious of the county they live in. Several counties have developed reputations for beauty, resorts, graceful living, or corruption. Recently two municipalities in corruption-ridden Hudson County have tried, so far unsuccessfully, to secede and join Bergen County.

New Jersey's first counties were formed after the colony's division into East and West Jersey in 1676. East Jersey set up four unnamed, vaguely bounded counties in 1675, but in 1683 gave them bounds and names: Bergen, Essex, Middlesex, and Monmouth. Somerset split off from Middlesex in 1688. In West Jersey, courts were established at Burlington and Salem in 1681, and by 1694 Burlington, Gloucester, Salem, and Cape May Counties were all in existence, but with incomplete boundaries. All the northern part of West Jersey, including the future Sussex, Warren, Morris, and Hunterdon Counties, was provisionally a part of Burlington County until 1714, when it was all formed into Hunterdon.

After the Jerseys were reunited in 1702, one of the early acts of the legislature resolved much of the vagueness of the early county boundaries. New counties came slowly: Hunterdon in 1714, Morris (including the future Sussex and Warren as well) from Hunterdon in 1739, Cumberland from Salem in 1748, and Sussex (including Warren) from Morris in 1753. War and other problems occupied New Jersey until 1824, when the fourteenth county, Warren, was formed from Sussex.

The leisurely pace came to an end, supplanted by a headlong rush for new counties; seven more were formed by 1857. The upheaval seems to have been traumatic: no new counties have been formed since. Rural Atlantic and urban Passaic Counties were formed on the same day in 1837, from Gloucester, Essex and Bergen. Mercer was born from four of its neighbors the next year, Hudson from Bergen in 1840, Camden from Gloucester in 1844, Ocean from Monmouth in 1850 and finally Union County from Essex in 1857.

Few counties remained content with their original boundaries. Over three dozen annexations have occurred, ranging from whole townships to a quarter acre, but since 1891 the changes have been small enough not to be noticeable to the casual map reader. One major map maker failed to correct his New Jersey maps for a moderate transfer of 1928, until it was brought to his attention in 1965.

Some smaller but recognizable changes in county and municipal lines are still ignored on large-scale county maps, in addition to state road maps. Monmouth County's official map of as late as 1967, for example, overlooks some Matawan land which the county has held within its bounds since 1939, and which appears on an earlier commercial street map published by the same map maker hired by the county for the official map. This was corrected by the 1971 edition. The official state outline map, revised in 1971, and the official U.S. census map of 1970, both showing county and municipal outlines, have minor errors. Occasionally inconsistent, they are both wrong in a couple of areas. So is a similar map the author prepared using earlier versions of these maps and other sources to attempt a completely accurate map.

One obstacle to showing accurate municipal boundaries is the elusiveness of the information. Three dozen townships were formed before 1700. By 1834 there were 125. During the century before 1875 all boundaries were described by state or provincial laws and were available in widely distributed law books. Since that time, the local municipality could vote itself into existence in a number of cases, and for over fifty years all municipalities have been allowed to annex by local ordinance. There are now 567 municipalities in New Jersey. Although the law requires filing of annexation ordinances with the county and state, this is frequently overlooked or ignored. The map makers' sleuths for accuracy can well be faced with a barrage of misinformation and out-of-date base maps unless they know when to probe rather than accept. It may not be considered worth the time and money.

CHANGING PLACE NAMES

Whether or not municipal or even county boundaries are shown on maps of New Jersey, the names of rivers, towns, and communities are essential on all but special outline maps. Rural townships are best known by the names of the unincorporated communities in them, except where legal matters are involved.

The names on a New Jersey map came from a variety of sources. Indian words formed the basis for many—Hackensack, Hohokus, Passaic, Musconetcong, Matawan, etc. Tributes to the great are obvious in scores of others; there are six Washington Townships, a Washington Borough, Washington Crossing, and a small crossroads community named Washington. There have been six Franklin Townships (four still exist), and Franklin and Franklin Lakes Boroughs are on current maps. Most were named for Benjamin, but one Franklin Township (now Wyckoff in Bergen County) was named for his son William, the last royal governor of the province.

Presidents Jefferson, Madison (twice), Monroe (twice), Jackson, W. H. Harrison (twice), Lincoln, Garfield, Roosevelt (both Theodore and Franklin) and Harding have also been recognized by municipal names past or present. Strangely, Cleveland—born in New

Jersey—and Wilson, elected President while governor of New Jersey, are both ignored in town names. Often the name perpetuates the name of a local industrialist, family or landowner—Longport, Mullica, Haddonfield and Hightstown are examples.

Scenery or location prompted names like Summit, Westfield, Belmar, Pleasantville, and Upper Township. Sentiment for homes in England led to Gloucester, Burlington, Manchester, Newark, Sussex, etc. (Sussex, Jersey's northernmost county, originally meant south Saxony.)

Name-changing can make it difficult to compare some places on old maps with new. Reasons for changes are sometimes obscure, but occasionally need little explanation. New Germantown and German Valley became Oldwick and Long Valley, respectively, during the anti-German hysteria of the First World War. Maidenhead became Lawrenceville soon after Burlington's famous Captain James Lawrence climaxed his naval career in the war of 1812 with the phrase "Don't give up the ship." In 1834, temperance-minded village leaders in southeast Morris County thought James Madison deserved perpetuation rather than a tavern symbol at Bottle Hill.

Caldwell Township wanted its own post office. To avoid confusion with Caldwell Borough, voters passed a referendum in November 1963 to change the name to Fairfield Township. They had not looked far enough: there had been a Fairfield Township in Cumberland County since 1697. Another referendum would have taken too long, so the legislature took pity and changed the name in June 1964 to Fairfield Borough. This satisfied the Post Office Department, and, since the municipality is organized under a Faulkner Act form of government which does not depend on Fairfield's being a township or a borough, the change was almost entirely limited to paper work.

Many early place names have disappeared from maps because they became ghost towns, or because they were absorbed by larger cities. The towns of Bergen, Paulus Hook, Wheatsheaf, and Chambersburg were absorbed into Jersey City, Linden, and Trenton.

The spelling of some place names can foil the most exacting, if they are unaware of the fact that it is Hohokus Brook, but Ho-Ho-Kus Borough (a common error on maps), River Vale but Northvale, Liberty Corner not Corners, and Wood-Ridge but Basking Ridge. Fair Lawn was officially Fairlawn before 1933, so it takes more than reasoning to establish the correct spelling. The subject of place names is a hobby and profession of its own.

THOSE TOPOGRAPHIC QUADRANGLES

New Jersey's topographic survey and Atlas Sheets of the 1880's established the state's shape with modern scientific accuracy. The U.S. Geological Survey, however, had funded and overseen the last half of the survey and soon was preparing its own topographic maps. That agency was eventually to produce maps which are probably more popular than the state's maps, due to their larger scale and lower price (although for a reduced area).

The U.S. Geological Survey was organized in 1879 under the Department of the Interior. Like the New Jersey Geological Survey, it was to concentrate on studying the mineral resources of the country —at first only in the western half, and with topographic maps only incidental to its work. Public demand for detailed maps eventually led to a complete reversal of its emphasis. Less than 7% of its maps are now published for geological work.[6]

Its first New Jersey maps were at almost the same scale as the State Atlas Sheets, 0.99 miles/inch, but covering less area, only 15 minutes of latitude and longitude. They were called quadrangles, and were revised into the early 1940's on a rather sporadic basis. Often they were merely reprinted, as late as fifty years after the last revision. About half of the state is also shown on 30' quadrangles, at 1.97 miles/inch (1:125,000 or 1/250,000th of true scale), but these maps were never revised after the first issues of 1899 to 1907.

The Geological Survey shifted to resurveys, begun in 1934, which led to a series of 7½-minute quadrangles at about twice the old scale, or ½ mile/inch. The Army Map Service joined the effort with its own surveying and large-scale mapping at a still different scale, much of it by aerial photography, during the 1940's. The U.S. Geological Survey changed once again by shifting in 1944 to a yet larger scale of 2,000 feet/inch (or 1:24,000) and issuing 7½-minute quadrangles (about 6 by 8 miles) covering the entire state by the mid-1950's. Its data came from new surveys as well as the combined results of the

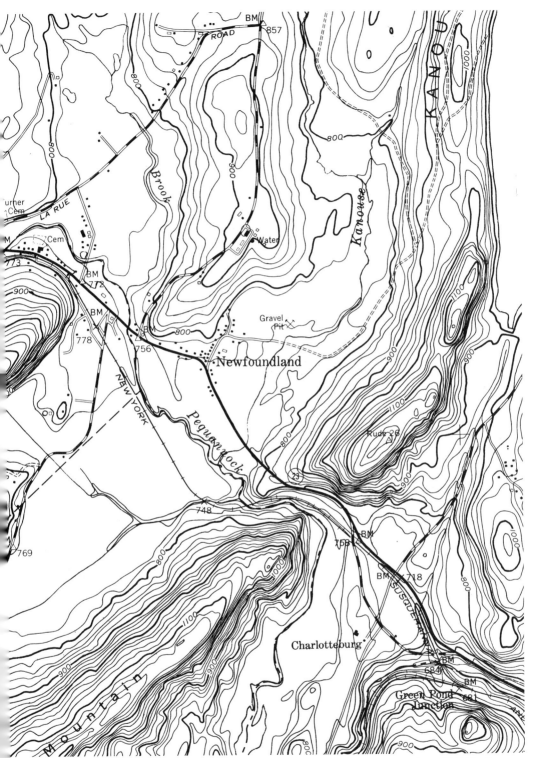

Detail from the U.S. Geological Survey *Newfoundland* quadrangle, issued at 2000'/inch with 20' contours. The area is part of that shown in the preceding details from the N.J. Geological Survey Atlas Sheets.

earlier mapping by the Army Map Service, Coast and Geodetic Survey, and the Geological Survey.[7]

These new quadrangles are the most accurate and detailed (and yet attractive and legible) maps available of most parts of New Jersey. Every house and principal building is shown except in built-up areas where a pink tint indicates an area in which only schools and other landmarks are shown. Contours are shown at twenty-foot intervals in hilly areas, and at ten- and five-foot intervals in flatter areas. All roads are shown, but only a few are named. Woodlands are shown in green, and the place names, rivers and lakes are added details making the quadrangles ideal bases for smaller scale maps.

The goal for updating the 7½-minute quadrangles is once every ten years, but the cost and the pressure of other work have resulted in minimal updating of the federal topographic maps of Jersey since the mid-1950's. Six date back to the 1940's. The price of each quadrangle is 75¢ when purchased directly from Washington. The Appendix lists each edition.

The New Jersey Geological Survey planned to issue its own set of large-scale topographic maps, but abandoned the project after only a quarter of the state was completed at 2,000 feet/inch. The last new map of the series appeared in 1905, but most. were revised over the next forty years. Since federal quadrangles now cover the entire state at the same scale, duplication by the state would be a needless expense.

The state continues to issue its own topographic Atlas Sheets, which are drawn, as stated earlier, to a scale of exactly 1 mile/inch, each sheet covering 28' of latitude and 26' of longitude. As with the U.S.G.S. maps, the goal for revision is every ten years, but several of these maps are fifteen to twenty years old. Omitting houses and buildings, they carry most of the other features of the larger-scale U.S. topographic maps, and sometimes have more frequent contour intervals. They are therefore more crowded and sometimes less legible to the point of making the light brown contours very difficult to follow, especially against street lines in built-up areas. They fill a need in providing detailed information in more compact form than the U.S. topo's, due to the smaller scale and larger area per map. Printing costs have soared, the sale price rising from 60¢ to the present $4.00 each in less than fifteen years.

ARMY MAPS FOR CIVILIANS

In addition to sharing the work of the U.S. Geological Survey in recent years, the Army Map Service prepares topographic maps at a scale of about four miles to the inch (1:250,000) which are both unique and attractive. These maps are two degrees of longitude wide (bounded by even degrees) and one degree of latitude high. Thus it takes six maps to cover *all* of New Jersey, but much of Delaware, Connecticut, eastern Pennsylvania and southern New York State are included as well. With one hundred-foot (and sometimes closer) contours, green woodlands overprint, yellow built-up areas, main roads in red, railroads, county lines and towns, the maps present pleasant, although somewhat overcontrasted, natural pictures of the area. They are available from the U.S. Geological Survey for $1.00 each, in flat paper form.

Much more appealing (and more expensive) are raised plastic relief sheets of three of the same maps, in the hilly north and central Jersey areas only, from 40° north latitude (Philadelphia) north, except for the Palisades and Atlantic highlands east of 74° west longitude. The vertical (third-dimensional) scale is three times horizontal, and the contour lines—still shown—are no longer the hard-to-interpret mazes of the flat map. During the 1950's and 1960's they were sold by the Army Map Service, but were cut from their budget in 1970. They are now sold by a private firm (see the Appendix). One other recent plastic relief map of New Jersey was prepared at the same 1:250,000 scale in one sheet by a commercial map maker, Aero Service Corp. of Philadelphia, in 1954, with a varying vertical exaggeration which reaches ten times in flat south Jersey.

MAPS OF THE SHORES

The U.S. Coast and Geodetic Survey, and now the National Ocean Survey, has prepared a variety of maps primarily for professional use, overlapping Geological Survey maps, but it is best known for its nautical charts. These cover all parts of the Jersey shore and the Delaware Bay and River up to Trenton, at scales of 1:10,000 to 1:80,000, and prices of 25¢ to $1.00. Depths of water and other nautical information are given, while adjacent land areas are shown with limited detail. These maps have been recently assembled in edited and book form.[8]

FLAT MAPS FOR A CURVED STATE: PROJECTIONS

When applied to an area as small as the state of New Jersey, the selection of an appropriate map projection would seem almost academic. Since a map projection is a graphical means of showing the doubly curved earth's surface on a flat plane, the error in using "any old projection" is partly a function of how much "double-curving" there is. Even the predominant north-south curved expanse of New Jersey by itself does not call for a special projection, since it could have been rolled on a cylinder, which can be accurately developed on a plane without distortion.

New Jersey, however, curves in both directions, and the east-west dimension is enough to result in a scale variation of one part in 13,000 when one of the most accurate flat projections for New Jersey—the Transverse Mercator—is used. On a map with a scale of 4 miles/inch, the largest scale normally used for a single map of the complete state, this is a variation of only about 1/300th of an inch in the true length of the yard-long line from High Point to Cape May. As if this were not a small enough error, the official scale of the Jersey map laid out according to this projection is made intermediate between the extremes of scale error (but deliberately not halfway), so that the yardstick is never more than 1/550th of an inch off, and usually much closer.

The Transverse Mercator is not the only available projection, however. If the most rudimentary projection were used for New Jersey, namely, one in which the parallels of latitude were horizontal equidistant lines and the meridians vertical equidistant lines, spaced at the right distance in the center of the map, the error would be one part in 36 instead of one part in 13,000. This would be far from a negligible error. Although several projections would be much more accurate than this "Rectangular Projection," it becomes apparent that projection does make a difference—even in little New Jersey.

A MERCATOR MAP ON ITS SIDE

The Transverse Mercator Projection mentioned above can be described as a Mercator map on its side. Most geography students have seen maps of the world drawn to the Mercator projection, with such gross exaggeration of areas in the polar regions that Greenland appears larger than South America even though only one-eighth the area. While atlases are increasingly stressing other projections for world maps, the Mercator does have merit. It is a conformal projection in that the shape of any small area on the globe is not distorted on this map (except at the poles). Near the equator the variation of scale is very slight, and the map is easily constructed. The projection is named for Gerardus Mercator, the Dutch map maker, who portrayed it first in a world map of 1569. It was not mathematically analyzed until thirty years later, by Edward Wright of Cambridge, England.

By rotating the grid of latitudes and longitudes on the globe until the equator runs through the north and south poles, as well as through New Jersey (or any other chosen area), we can then draw a map of the world in accordance with a Mercator projection based on this rotated equator. This is called the Transverse Mercator Projection. While rather involved mathematics is necessary to calculate the positions on the map for intersections of the various actual latitudes and longitudes, this has been done by the federal government for every 2½ minutes of each in the New Jersey area, and the resulting table can be purchased for 25¢.[9]

NEW JERSEY RECEIVES A GRID SYSTEM

Since there are several good map projections for New Jersey, and since most of them permit selection of any one of a variety of "cen-

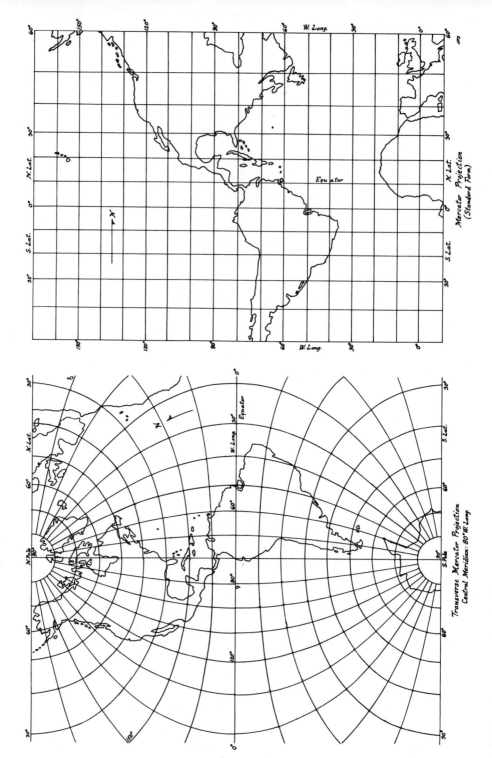

An outline map of the Americas according to the regular and the transverse Mercator projections. The scale remains constant along any line from left to right; thus the Americas appear less distorted on the Transverse Projection, because of their predominant north-south direction. The shapes of all small elements are correctly shown.

tral meridians" or "standard parallels," the need for standardization was felt early in the twentieth century. The various refinements in measuring the slight oblateness (flatness) of the earth's shape compounded the problem of plotting geodetic triangulation points accurately on maps drawn on different grids to different projections. The mathematics could be overwhelming.

The United States Coast and Geodetic Survey, beginning in 1933, began to develop standard coordinate systems for each state, in order to achieve the least distortion. The states with predominantly north-south directions, including New Jersey, received coordinate systems based on the Transverse Mercator Projection. Those with predominant east-west expanse were given systems based on the Lambert Conformal Conic Projection. Systems for Florida and New York involve both projections. Most states are divided into several map zones by the U.S.C.&G.S., each with its own central meridian (which corresponds to the equator of our rotated globe) or its own standard parallels (if the Lambert system is involved). New Jersey and several other small states are given only one zone.[10] The central meridian for this state is 74° 40' West Longitude, which passes near High Point, Trenton, and Ocean City.

In 1935 the New Jersey legislature became the first in the nation to put the Plane Coordinate System, as the U.S.C.&G.S. mapping system is called, into law. In view of the vigorous opposition to this step by title companies who felt that property descriptions would not be concise enough if based solely on coordinates of lot corners, the act includes a clause permitting the use of other surveying systems as well.[11] Since the passage of the law, several county and municipal boundaries have been clarified or changed in terms of the Plane Coordinate System.

When boundaries are described according to this system, the x and y coordinates, in feet, are given for monuments along the boundary lines. The y-coordinate is measured north from a line at 38° 50' north latitude, just below Cape May. The x-coordinate is measured east or west from the central meridian, which is given a reading of two million feet so there are no negative values. The measurement increases going east.

The detailed topographic maps issued by the U.S. Geological Survey will sometimes show tick marks around the edges indicating not only latitude and longitude, but also reference coordinates according to the Plane Coordinate System. If so, they are given in feet, some-times with the last three or four zeroes omitted.

There are two other coordinate systems which may be shown on the topographic maps and on a few of the official county maps of New Jersey. These systems were designed for world-wide use. A few decades ago, the Progressive Military Grid was in use. If the coordi-nates on an older map are given in yards, this is probably the grid referred to. Zone A, which included all of New Jersey, consisted of a grid laid on a polyconic projection with 73° 00′ West Longitude as the central meridian. The point at 40° 30′ North Latitude on the central meridian had an x-coordinate of 1,000,000 yards and a y-value of 2,000,000 yards. The readings increased to the east and to the north, respectively.

The Progressive Military Grid has been replaced by the Universal Transverse Mercator Grid (UTM). The projection, as the name im-plies, is the same as that used in the Plane Coordinate System, but the center is different, and the scale is given in meters. The central meridian is 75° 00′ West Longitude for the six-degree-wide zone including New Jersey, and its x-coordinate is 500,000 meters. The vertical (y) measurement, however, begins at the equator, so that Trenton has a y-coordinate of about 4,450,000 meters.

Since the central meridians on all three of these grid systems are different, and one has a different projection, the three grids are tilted slightly with respect to each other. The coordinates on one system are therefore not easily converted to another grid system without extensive tables. This will not bother most cartophiles, who will generally be satisfied just to know what the tick marks refer to.

Actually, not many of the government maps of New Jersey are constructed according to the Transverse Mercator Projection. The two-degree by one-degree Army Map Service maps at about 4 miles/inch, mentioned above, and the AMS quadrangles are based on this projection, but none of the other maps we have mentioned is known to use it.

A MAP FROM MANY CONES

The polyconic projection referred to earlier is the standard map used in the topographical quadrangles prepared by the U.S. Geological Survey, as well as in the Atlas Sheets of the New Jersey Geological Survey. This projection was invented about 1820 by Ferdinand Hassler, the first Superintendent of the U.S. Coast Survey.[12] It was popular among map makers because universal tables could be calculated, making it easy to construct. Like the Transverse Mercator Projection, it has a central meridian which is a straight line, and which is marked off with latitudes at their true distances on the corresponding globe.

Each parallel of latitude is shown as part of a circle with a radius which can be determined in this way: If a ruler is laid in a north-south direction on the globe at a given latitude so it is tangent to the globe, a northward extension of the ruler will intersect an extension of the globe's axis somewhere in space. The distance along the ruler from the tangent point to the point of intersection with the globe's axis is the radius of that parallel of latitude on the polyconic map. As a result, the parallels are not concentric, but are constructed as if various tangent cones are being unfolded around the central meridian. The longitudes are then marked off on each circular latitude at their true distances on the globe.

The projection is not completely free from distortion in area, shape, or scale, but when it is applied to quadrangles only 7½ minutes of latitude by 7½ minutes of longitude, it hardly matters. It is convenient for the map maker and provides considerable accuracy.

JOHANN LAMBERT'S CONIC MAP

Used on a number of commercial maps of New Jersey, the Lambert Conformal Conic Projection, like the Transverse Mercator, maintains the correct shape for each small area. Its parallels of latitude are arcs of concentric circles with the meridians serving as equally spaced radii of the circles. The circles are not quite equally spaced, but have radii calculated from a rather complex formula designed so that the scale is correct along two "standard" parallels—one near the top and one near the bottom of the map. It was invented in 1772 by Johann Heinrich Lambert, an Alsatian mathematician, who also devised the Transverse Mercator Projection in the same year.[13]

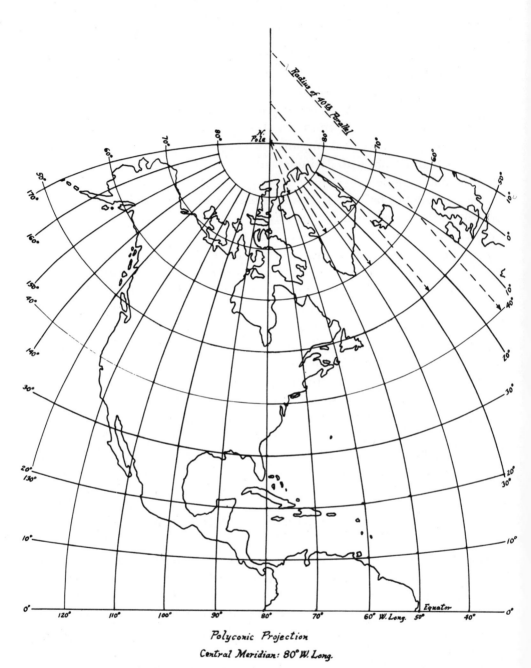

Polyconic Projection

Central Meridian: 80° W. Long.

North America on a polyconic projection grid. The parallels are arcs of circles which are not concentric, but have radii equal to the sides of cones tangent to the sphere at the respective latitudes. The meridians are complex curves formed by connecting points ticked off along the parallels at their true distances.

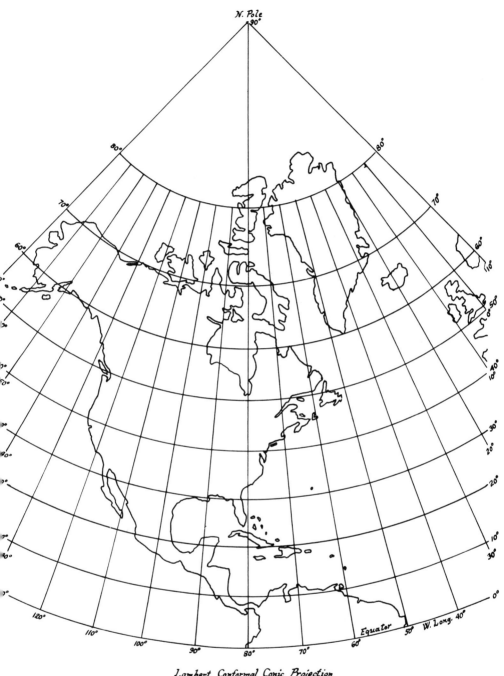

Lambert Conformal Conic Projection
Standard Parallels: 10° & 48°40′ N. Lat.

A grid of Lambert's conformal conic projection. Meridians are straight lines radiating from the center of the concentric circles forming the parallels. The parallels are not equally spaced, however. Like the Mercator projections, this projection shows the shapes of all small segments correctly.

TO MAKE A MODERN SURVEY

Surveying of large areas has been revolutionized during the twentieth century by the use of aerial photography, but ground surveying has also had its share of major improvements. The mainstay instruments of ground surveying are still the transit, tape, level, and rod. The rod is held vertically and is clearly graduated in tenths of a foot with a vernier for hundredths of a foot. The level, a horizontal swivel telescope mounted on a tripod, is used to sight readings on the rod held at two or more marked points on the ground or on monuments, such as official bench marks. The difference between the elevations of the various monuments is then determined from the readings.

The tape is stretched out between two points to measure the distance. The steel strip, 5 to 500 feet in length, and ⅛ to ½ inch wide, is graduated in feet, with decimals of a foot at one end. Temperature, tension, and sag corrections must all be included to make the reading accurate.

The transit is a less elegant relative of the theodolite, consisting of a telescope and compass mounted on a tripod. The telescope can be swung both horizontally and vertically, the angles being carefully measured with scales and verniers built into the instrument.

The transit and tape are companions in horizontal surveying. While distances and directions can be measured over large areas by moving the transit to many locations whose distances are taped, triangulation is much faster. An integral part of the geodetic surveying of New Jersey in the 1880's, triangulation minimizes the taping of distances by making use of a large number of horizontal angular measurements from a small number of transit locations.

Sometimes, when large bodies of water or deep ravines are involved, triangulation is the only practical means of survey, since taping becomes nearly impossible. By locating the transit at two positions whose distance apart can be taped, a base line is established for a series of triangles which will locate the inaccessible points. Triangulation has been modernized with the use of electro-optical distance-measuring instruments (EODMI) which permit trilateration, a faster technique.[14]

Plane surveying disregards the curvature of the earth's surface, and therefore is adequate for small areas. Geodetic surveying, on the other hand, recognizes the curvature and is essential for an area which is more than a few miles square.

Automation has come to ground surveying and includes such devices as the Johnson elevation meter, an instrument in a special vehicle which continuously measures slope changes along a road with a totalizing circuit. The vehicle may travel up to twenty-five miles per hour, producing up to one hundred miles of level lines per day.[15]

Laser beams are being used to measure distances of up to 4½ miles with an accuracy of ⅜ inch. One instrument resembles a camera mounted on a tripod and powered with a 12-volt portable battery. The laser beam is aimed at a reflector which has been spotted from the transmitter, and the travel time is measured by the instrument and converted to distance. One twenty-six-day project (by older methods) took two days by laser instrument.[16]

Aerial photographic mapping is probably the greatest advance in large area surveying. Measuring by photography is called photogrammetry. The camera lens must be of extra-high precision to minimize distortion around the edges. The camera should also be pointed straight down from the aircraft, to keep the scale uniform. By getting well-overlapped photos from the air, the mappers on the ground can compare the photos with the use of complex instruments, and correct for any distortion and nonvertical position of the camera.

One of the most intriguing uses of aerial photography is direct plotting of contour lines on maps of the area by stereophotogrammetry—a system of instruments which measures heights of land from overlapping photos much as a stereoptic viewer "shows" three dimensions from two flat photographs taken from different points.[17] Most of the current U.S. Geological Survey's 7½′ quadrangles in north Jersey received their contour lines in this manner.

As an example of one more innovation, aerial photography with "false-color" infrared color film was recently used to rechart the boundaries of New Jersey's coastal wetlands. Since different types of vegetation reflect infrared light differently, types which grow in salt water can be distinguished by experts from types which require fresh water, when using the infrared film. The wetlands boundary is thus established at less than a tenth of the cost of a ground survey.[18]

THE MAP-MAKING INDUSTRY

Unlike Lewis Evans, Thomas Gordon, and the other private map makers of their day, modern commercial map makers rarely have to make field surveys. The government has done the surveying for them, and they are as free to use it as the rest of the public. Many companies have now produced detailed maps of New Jersey, usually for road maps or atlases. Two of the best-known commercial map makers have Jersey headquarters: General Drafting and Hammond. Both moved from New York City about twenty years ago.

A brief description of each company makes an interesting modern-day contrast with the Erskines and the Colleses.

GENERAL DRAFTING CO.: ROAD MAPS
WITH FINESSE

General Drafting Co., Inc., made the move in 1952, after forty-three years in various Manhattan locations, to a forty-two-room, Tudor-style mansion in a residential area of Convent Station, N.J., near Morristown. The mansion was only thirty-five years old at the time, but it was patterned after a castle completed in 1528 in War-wickshire, England. Making as few structural changes as possible, the company made certain that the old English atmosphere, complete with ivy, continues to dominate the scene for the approaching visitor.[19]

The company was founded in 1909 by a twenty-three-year-old Finn named Otto Gustave Lindberg, who had arrived in America just two years earlier. Shortly after his birth in St. Petersburg (now Leningrad), Russia, in 1886, his family moved to Helsingfors (Helsinki), where his father became manager of a factory. There the youth studied drafting and other subjects at Technical University. After two years of study, he succumbed to the vivid tales of opportunity in America, which he contrasted with the strong political pressures exerted in Russian-dominated Finland. He left in 1907,

The headquarters of General Drafting Co., Inc., Convent Station, N.J. Built in 1917, it was patterned after an English castle built in 1528. The map-making firm moved there from New York City in 1952. *General Drafting Co., Inc.*

after convincing his father that he should go to America when he failed two difficult math courses.

Lindberg's first job in America was on the night shift of a paper mill in Rumford Falls, Maine, at 17½ cents per hour. He was promoted to draftsman there, but after three months in the U.S., he switched to a succession of drafting jobs in Yonkers, Tarrytown, and New York City. It was late in 1909 that he was struck with the thought of becoming a public draftsman, for contract hire like a public stenographer. Thus was born General Drafting Co., but the jobs were few and varied. The American Automobile Association gave him his first map jobs—five small road maps in 1911. The AAA was also the source of his first map project for a whole state, Vermont, which was done without visiting the state. This was his last touring map for several years, and other mapping ventures put him $25,000 in debt by 1919.

Other map companies were following AAA's lead with road maps sold at 25¢ to $1.00 a copy, but accuracy and legibility were often limited. Lindberg's attempts to use existing road maps on trips frustrated him so much that he decided he had to make better ones. In 1922 the First National Bank of Boston asked him to make a map of Massachusetts. This time he field-checked his source material by touring the state. The bank distributed the maps free—a successful idea which spurred Lindberg to try the idea on an oil company to help them sell more gasoline. Living in Westfield, N.J., where he moved in 1911 and remained until his death, he picked a New Jersey-based oil company as his prospective client. In 1923 he was able to persuade Standard Oil Co. of New Jersey to let him draw the "best" road map of New Jersey that they had ever seen, for free distribution. If they were dissatisfied, they weren't to pay him!

Standard was impressed by the product and contracted with him to make all their road maps. General Drafting still does. The legibility and accuracy of his maps resulted from many innovations, not the least of which was his personal checking, at first, of the road conditions. Starting with simple red, black, and white maps, the maps have improved with wise choices of color, type size and spacing, complete indexing, and the addition of information about bridges, tolls, construction work, and so on. General Drafting now makes, in the estimation of many (including this writer), an outstandingly attractive road map design, unexcelled in the U.S.[20]

The company's contracts extend well beyond Esso Standard Oil (now Exxon Corp.), but not with other oil companies; the map maker refuses to consider others. They also encompass touring service and numerous guidebooks and maps not related to roads. The eighty-member staff has also prepared its first world atlas, the *Odyssey,* and a related "thematic" atlas stressing geography. Instead of surveying, the company relies on uncopyrighted base maps—usually government maps such as those described—and applies its own on-the-site research to minimize errors.

The first step in General Drafting's map making consists of photographing the base maps and cutting the negatives into pieces which are fitted together into a mosaic twice the scale of the map to be printed. A blue-line print of the mosaic is made on a plastic sheet, on which the compiler draftsman then draws and traces the features wanted on the final map. Names are hand-lettered to the size desired. After careful office and field checking and correcting, the draft copy is reprinted on a plastic film with a soft emulsion. This film is the base for the final map, on which roads and other lines are etched in with a sapphire-tipped tool. Names set in type are pasted on an overlay of the map.[21]

Some six to twelve months after the map work begins, the map is ready for publication. General Drafting subcontracts all its printing to lithographers all across the United States. Offset lithography is specified, usually in four press colors for road maps: yellow, light blue, red, and dark blue. Other colors result from overlap. The maps are usually printed four to a sheet and up to 5,000 sheets per hour.[22]

Publishing over 20 million maps a year, General Drafting is third in volume after Rand McNally and H. M. Gousha, the leaders in road map volume.[23] Founder Otto Lindberg died in 1968 at the age of 81, three years after retiring as president. He was succeeded by Finnish-born Arne Kauppinen who was in turn followed by Richard E. Scully. The latter is now chairman of the board, and Joachim J. Adamczyk is president.

Otto Gustave Lindberg (1886–1968), founder and long-time president of General Drafting Co., Inc. Having spent his early years in Finland, he founded the company in 1909, after two years in America. *General Drafting Co., Inc.*

HAMMOND INC.: PERSPECTIVE ON THE WORLD

Hammond, a somewhat different type of map company, moved from New York City to Maplewood, N.J., in 1950. Out of the road map field since 1931, except for some street maps, Hammond is most famous for atlases, globes, and related school materials.

Caleb Stillson Hammond founded the company in New York City in 1900, after reportedly being refused a $5-a-week raise by Rand McNally, where he was a district sales manager. He had been born in Rush, New York, near Rochester, in 1862. As a teenager in Ironia, Michigan, he became a reporter for the daily *Grand Rapids Sentinel,* until he started his own daily in Ironia. Selling out profitably to the *Sentinel,* he moved to Chicago, where he soon began working for Rand McNally. At twenty-four, Hammond married and moved to New York City to open a branch store for his employer. He made the break to form his own company after fourteen years in the East.

Hammond's first map, a reversible which was unique at the time, showed U.S. railroads on one side, a world map on the other. Its success was followed by incorporation as C. S. Hammond & Co. in December 1901. The first "& Co." are said to have been his wife and sister, who did the indexing. C.S.H., his brother, and his brother-in-law constituted the investors and first officers.

The small staff put out a sign, "Maps of Everywhere," and by 1906 had printed a world atlas (which sold millions) and had produced the first "instant book"—a collection of San Francisco earthquake photographs published three days after the event. The next four years saw Hammond branching into road maps as well with a *Road Atlas of Long Island* and *Auto Route Distance Maps—New England to Ohio.*

In 1911 the company pioneered again by opening a retail map store at the Hudson Terminal in New York. Now in midtown Manhattan, the store handles not only Hammond maps and globes, but government maps and publications of competitors as well. By 1929, the growing firm had had five successive New York City addresses, and two in Brooklyn. A Boston retail store had opened, but was soon to close. The founder also died in 1929, to be succeeded as

Caleb Stillson Hammond (1862–1929), who founded the map company bearing his name in 1900. Like General Drafting, the company was started in New York City. It was moved to Maplewood, N.J., in 1950. *Hammond Inc.*

president by his eldest son. Hammond's first globes appeared in 1930, but the company was entering a depression of its own which lasted until the Second World War. After three more New York addresses, Hammond made the move to its one New Jersey location of the last twenty years.[24]

At last innovations began to take hold to make Hammond a leader in the field. The company has recently developed new types of globes—inflatable plastic in the 1950's and, of course, moon globes in the 1960's. It grants a cartography scholarship at Northwestern University and a Library Award for contributions to the increased interest in maps.

Reaching beyond the map world, Hammond has issued collections of Audubon prints, Currier & Ives lithographs, old maps, and nature and travel books, in all of which they can extend their talents for beautiful, precise, multicolor printing. But they are still essentially map makers and produce over a billion maps per year. One of their most recent innovations was a new line of *Perspective* atlases, first produced in 1966, which place all material for the country or state on adjacent pages. Besides the main full-page map with towns and color-bordered subdivisions, Hammond includes a shaded relief map, an economic map, a highway or special map, and the complete map index, all before passing to the next area.

After a skilled draftsman draws at a large scale a new map or revises an old one, the drawing is photographed, and the negative, after checking, goes to the plate-making department for offset printing plates. Hammond does some of its own printing on three small presses in Maplewood, but it subcontracts most of it. It also has its own Linotype for setting up type for place names. It has developed not only expert techniques for printing on paper; it also prints on plastic (for three-dimensional maps and inflatable globes) and produces map transparencies for overhead projectors in classrooms.

The company has recently entered the increasingly popular field of making three-dimensional relief maps. Instead of the older techniques of cardboard or plaster layers to conform with the contours, an aluminum alloy sheet, printed with contours, is pressed up by hand from below to give the proper shape. The underside is then filled in with clay. The resulting raised sheet can be painted as required, and then, with angle lighting, photographed completely or in part to produce a flat shaded relief map. It can also be made into a mold for the production of raised plastic facsimiles of the map.

Constant updating is a mixed blessing to any map maker; the work is grueling, but old maps are outdated, thus opening the door for increased sales. Hammond tries to keep up with hundreds of changes in its state maps, often involving name changes of small towns. To augment official census populations of incorporated towns, Hammond writes to thousands of postmasters of unincorporated towns for population estimates. Replies are occasionally more humorous than informative: "87 families, not including children," "7 people, 6 goats, 4 dogs," and "15 proud souls." [25] Correcting some maps involves a political problem, however, since some countries, like India and Pakistan, have very different opinions as to how a disputed area should be shown. Thus a map suitable for one country is contraband in the other. Hammond's day-by-day search of current sources is backed by its own 14,000-volume library, used by its staff of editors and compilers.

The company name was changed in 1966 to Hammond Inc., still chiefly family-owned and controlled. Two grandsons of the founder, Caleb D. and Stuart L. Hammond, are now chairman of the board and fifth president, respectively. The Maplewood headquarters has 125 employees, and the sales outlets have another seventy-five.[26]

MILLIONS FOR FREE: THE ROAD MAPS

By far the most used, road maps also have the most detail of any maps normally seen by the public. Although some companies, such as Hagstrom and Rand McNally, sell road maps to the public, most travelers automatically think of the gasoline station as the source of excellent free up-to-date road maps. This was not true before 1923.

Road maps of northern New Jersey began to appear in commercial quantities in the 1890's. Colton advertised maps of several northern counties. The Globe Map Co. bound a set of maps into a booklet advertising only bicycles. The League of American Wheelmen issued several editions of road maps for bicyclists beginning in 1890. The 1893 edition includes eight sectional maps of the state at two miles to the inch. In 1896, the *Road Book* changed to a reduced scale of 4 miles/inch, three miles in the north section. All roads are shown, the major ones in red. An index map and descriptive material complete the hardbound booklet.[27] Gústav Kobbé of Short Hills, N.J., was the best-known mapper, but he was equally famous as an author of articles with travel lore about the state, combining road maps with lucid narration.[28]

In 1901, The National Publishing Company of Boston brought out a New Jersey "Road Map" at 4 miles/inch complete with railroad mileages, town elevations, and colored outlines of each township and county, but differentiating only between "important" and "unimportant" roads. The Automobile Club of America, C. S. Mendenhall of Cincinnati, and others issued pocket-size guide and road maps of the state.

Road Map of New Jersey, detail. By National Publishing Co., 1901. An early detailed commercial highway map to appeal to the new motor car touring interest. Full size. *Rutgers University Library.*

By 1915, both Hammond (1906) and Rand McNally (undated) had issued detailed road maps of northern Jersey, Hammond at 3 miles/inch and Rand McNally at 1.8. Each distinguished between "improved or main automobile roads" and rough "highways"; both outlined all municipalities.[29]

The year 1910 saw fold-out sectional atlases of parts of New Jersey, issued as an *Official Road Map* by the New Jersey Automobile and Motor Club. Roads were indicated as fair, smooth, main, and unclassified. Trolley lines were also included. The scale, nowhere marked, was about 1 or 2 miles/inch depending on the area, and separate booklets were issued for various parts of the state. The dangers of driving were attested to by the speed limit note: "1 mile in 7 minutes on curves, 1 mile in 4 minutes at street intersections or within 200 feet of horses and animals on the highway, 1 mile in 5 minutes in built-up sections. Elsewhere—1 mile in 2 minutes 40 sections." [30]

In such a burgeoning field, map makers could be expected to come forth with new ideas in the attempt to sell America—and New Jersey—on the idea of increased use of automobiles, accessories—and gasoline. As stated earlier, General Drafting Co. was practically the founder of the free oil company road map. A synopsis of the changing format of its New Jersey road maps prepared for the Standard Oil Co. of New Jersey gives some idea of the rate at which map styles can change. Its first, in 1923, shows first-class roads in heavy red lines bordered in black—a wider black for "through routes," and narrower for "other roads." Second-class roads were drawn the same without the red, and "third class roads, usable in dry and settled weather" were single lines. There were nine sizes of towns, and hatchured mountain ranges, but only the colors red, black, and white.

General Drafting redrew the entire map in 1926, adding for the first time a date, railroads, and highway route numbers. There were now seven types of roads shown instead of five. In 1931 blue water and green or brown hills were added. The next year the hill coloring was dropped, but one year later green state park areas were added. Yellow now colored the neighboring states, and bordered New Jersey's counties as well.

In 1936 railroads were eliminated from the Standard Oil maps. Railroads are no longer found on oil company maps. While the addition of new roads may have crowded out the railroads, it was more likely that they were eliminated because the oil companies rejected the competition. After all, there was and still is room for railroads on the official state highway maps issued to about the same scale. Most railroads, however, are now only landmarks to the motorist, who can ride on very few of them.

From 1940 to 1953 a pictorial map of the state was added to the General Drafting sheet, and in 1961 the map was redrawn with revised symbols. Every map has included an enlargement of the New York metropolitan area in Jersey, and the Philadelphia, Trenton, and Atlantic City areas gradually found their places.

General Drafting Co. now chooses the largest commercial scale of all for its road map of Jersey, about 5.3 miles/inch. With cartographic precision, it names its projection (Lambert Conformal) and draws a grid coinciding with every 10′ of latitude and longitude. The grid is also labeled with large letters and numbers to help the indexing of towns. County boundaries are still emphasized with yellow, and county names are in large red print. Roads are given nine categories, and towns and cities just five, according to population. Northeast Jersey is enlarged (still "Lambert Conformal") to about 2 miles/inch.

Rand McNally & Co. of Chicago, most famous for atlases, produces Jersey road maps for oil companies and for its own *Road Atlas,* which contains enlarged maps of every state. Unlike General Drafting, it sells to several oil companies. On its larger map of New Jersey (5.6 miles/inch) it has a square index grid without relation to latitude and longitude. With the average motorist in mind, it merely marks 30-minute latitude and longitude ticks around the edge and identifies the counties with small print and fine boundary lines. It has ten road classifications and seven sizes of towns and cities. Rand McNally's *Road Atlas* map of New Jersey is smaller, at 8.2 miles/inch, and has no index grid, except at the edges.

In 1961, Rand McNally shifted from a two-color format to nine, but at the same time slightly reduced the precision of mapping in favor of more flowing and conspicuous main roads, fewer back roads and place names, and larger type for moderate-sized towns. The decision may be mourned from a purist standpoint, but there is no doubt that the new format is much more attractive and prob-

Detail of the first General Drafting Co. oil company road map of New Jersey, 1923, full size. Main highways are shown in red on actual map. Next four maps show changes in detail, roads, and artistry. © *General Drafting Co., Inc.*

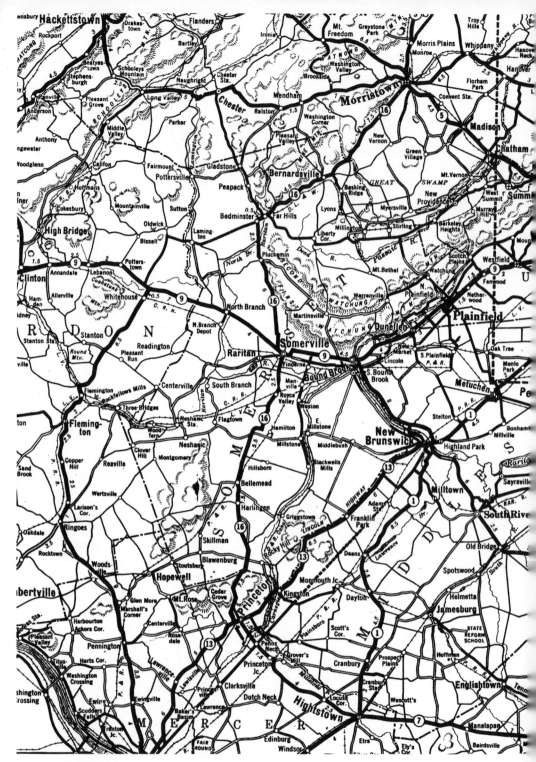

Detail of General Drafting's 1928 Standard Oil road map of New Jersey, full size. State highways (numbered according to the system of 1917–27) are red, other roads and details are dark blue on actual map. © *General Drafting Co., Inc.*

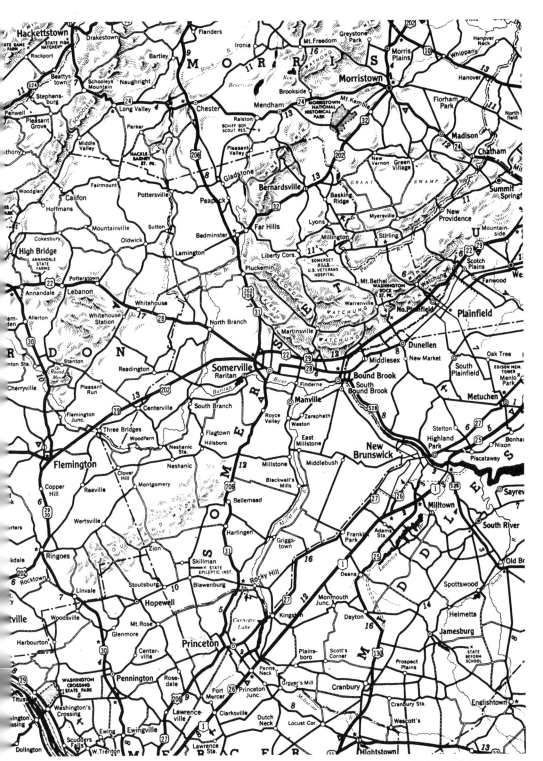

Detail of 1940 General Drafting Co. Esso road map of New Jersey, full size. Highway renumbering of 1927, missed on the 1928 map, continued until 1953 with additions. Actual map is colored red (main roads), dark blue (general), green (parks), light blue (water), and yellow (boundaries and larger towns). © *General Drafting Co., Inc.*

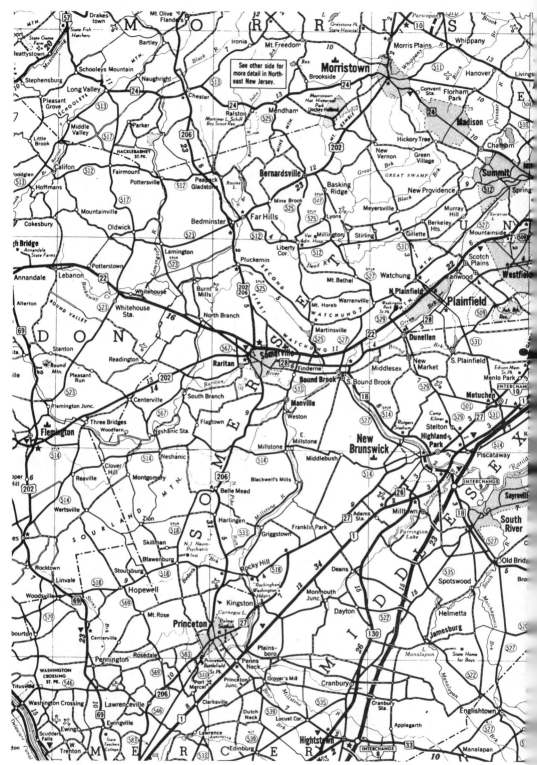

Detail of the 1955–56 Esso map of New Jersey by General Drafting Co., full size. Orange, for towns 10,000–25,000, is added to colors of 1940 version. The 1953 highway renumbering is evident. © *General Drafting Co., Inc.*

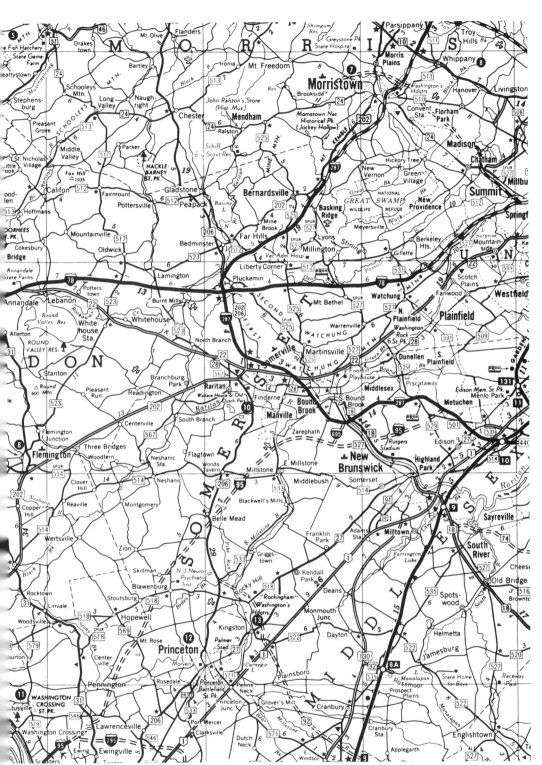

Detail of the first Exxon (formerly Esso) map of New Jersey by General Drafting Co., late 1972, full size. Local roads are shown single-line after 1961 redrafting. Incomplete Interstate highways sweep across map. © *General Drafting Co., Inc.*

ably more useful to those for whom it is intended: the traveler, not the cartophile.

The third titan of the road map field, H. M. Gousha Co. (pronounced goo-shay'), is commercially more like Rand McNally than General Drafting. It produces a road atlas for sale as well as maps for free distribution by several oil companies. It ignores latitude and longitude identification altogether, and de-emphasizes county names and boundaries. Although its Jersey map shows eleven types of roads and eight sizes of towns, it shows fewer back roads than its competitors on equal-sized maps. The nine-color oil company map scales at 6.7 miles/inch, but Gousha produced the same map—adding railroads—at a larger scale of 5.6 miles/inch for the New Jersey Department of Transportation in 1969.

The Big Three are not alone in the field, and competitors produce attractive maps at similar scales. For a small state, New Jersey is fortunate to be placed on a map of its own by almost all gasoline company road mappers. Other small states, like Rhode Island and Delaware, usually have to share a map with their neighbors.

The State of New Jersey, like most states, issues a free road map through its Department of Transportation. The 1917 law setting up the State Highway system declared that "The State Highway Commission shall from time to time cause to be prepared a road map or plan of the State showing thereon the State highways and county roads." [31] The state had already been doing this in some form since the turn of the century. Beginning about 1902, the Commissioner of Roads issued a map of "Improved Wagon Roads" at 5 miles/inch. It consisted of a black and white New Jersey Geological Survey base map, including townships and local roads, with a red-line overlay for "improved roads, built under the provisions of the State Law, together with some of the connecting roads, built by the local authorities, without State aid."

Until about 1910 this map was revised every couple of years. Then the base map was redrawn to a larger scale, 4 miles/inch. For the next decade and more, the official state "Road Map" consisted of red lines laid over the new base map, solid for roads "improved with State Aid" and dashed for roads "improved without State Aid." The 1918 map still had no highway route numbers, in spite of the law passed the year before authorizing the first fifteen numbered routes, but the 1921 map burst forth with all fifteen.

After two more annual revisions, the state shifted to a private concern for its official road map, and no longer showed township lines. General Drafting Co. was chosen, and used its oil company map prepared the year before, adding highway route numbers, and updating it. The map was issued in 1924 at 5.6 miles/inch. It shows mileage along main roads, but includes very few of the unimproved roads. The 1928 map shows the effects of the drastic route renumbering in 1927 (but ignores all federal highway numbers) and also includes the polite note that

In many instances, when a State Highway is to be constructed, additional property along the line of the highway must be acquired. The State Highway Commission extends thanks to those public spirited citizens who have deeded to the State the lands necessary for road building, for a nominal consideration. The general public should know that such acts are notable contributions to the cause of good roads.

(Was this euphemistic, or was it a far cry from the present-day "authoritarian tactics" which are attributed to the highway advance men as they secure the right-of-way through crowded areas?)

After annual revisions through 1931 by General Drafting, with vastly increased detail, many more colors, and large scale—up to 4.3 miles/inch, the state shifted to several other firms who bid lowest during the 1930's and 1940's. Except for 1939, the official map did not again fall to General Drafting until 1955, when the publisher began more than a decade of issuing the map as an eighteen-page booklet with sectional maps displaying separately colored counties.

In 1969, Gousha replaced General Drafting, and (by request) reverted to a single sheet, but in 1970 the state once again began producing the maps from its own drafting boards. The Department of Transportation declared that it wished to get away from the problem of copyright of a government-financed map, and to save money. For the 1970 map, the state again chose 4 miles/inch, the same as its maps fifty years earlier, and the same as some of the official maps by the Bureau of Geology and Topography, and by the Army Map Service. The map is attractively colored, but it emphasizes the state highway system to the point of showing local roads as almost inconsequential, and all classed as one kind. The county boundaries are thin orange lines, and the county names are almost invisible. The dozens of errors on the first edition were substantially reduced by the 1972 edition, but many of the remaining errors are too easily found.

On all the official road maps, the railroads have regularly appeared. With the marked decline of passenger routes, the very recent ones have used two railroad symbols, one for passenger lines, and one for freight only.

MAPS FOR THE ARMCHAIR: ATLASES

New Jersey maps which are parts of U.S. or world atlases make up, like maps of other states, a group quite distinct from road maps. On the one hand, the atlas cartographer is limited by a generally smaller scale to a map with fewer details. On the other, he no longer has to focus primarily on the needs of a single type of user, but can work toward a more artistic product. Therefore, there is a much wider variety of styles, and scales, depending on the size of the page.

Rand McNally, noted for more than a century of map making, strongly emphasized both county lines and railroads in their atlases of 1895 to 1950. Counties were solidly colored at first, and later outlined in orange, with a grid of half degrees of latitude and longitude. The accuracy was only moderate; for example, the northern boundary was shown as a straight line, instead of slightly bowed, and county boundaries were forty years behind in the 1932 atlas, and only partially updated by the 1949 edition.

The tendency to overcrowd the 1895 map with place names was gradually remedied as fewer names were shown. By 1967, the Rand McNally atlas was de-emphasizing counties with light blue lines for bounds and small print for names. Accuracy was much improved (the north boundary now had the proper bow in it), the projection (Lambert Conformal Conic) was identified, and printing was much more attractive. Railroads were shown as thin red lines; highways were still omitted. The shading of the large built-up areas in violet is a special asset of the newer maps.

Hammond Inc., the chief American competitor of Rand McNally in publishing world atlases, has come a long way since the early

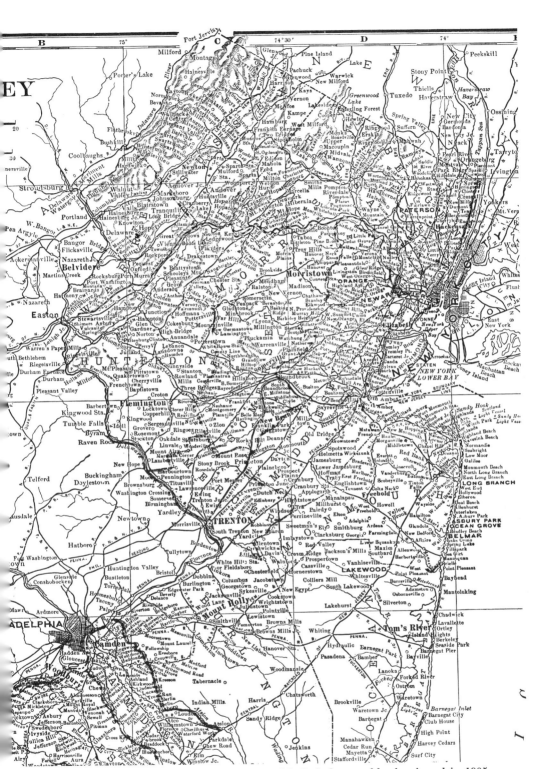

Most of New Jersey, as shown in C. S. Hammond & Co.'s first world atlas, issued in 1905. Each county was given a separate solid color. Map was copyrighted 1903 and is reproduced full size. © *Hammond Inc.*

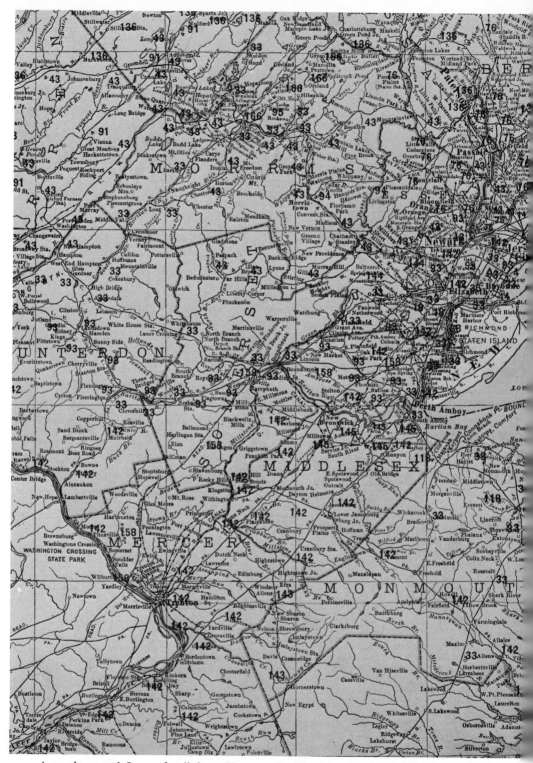

A north central Jersey detail from Hammond's *The New-World Loose Leaf Atlas*, late 1920's (undated). A pink map with blue county outlines, railroads are identified with large red numbers and a key. Full size. © *Hammond Inc.*

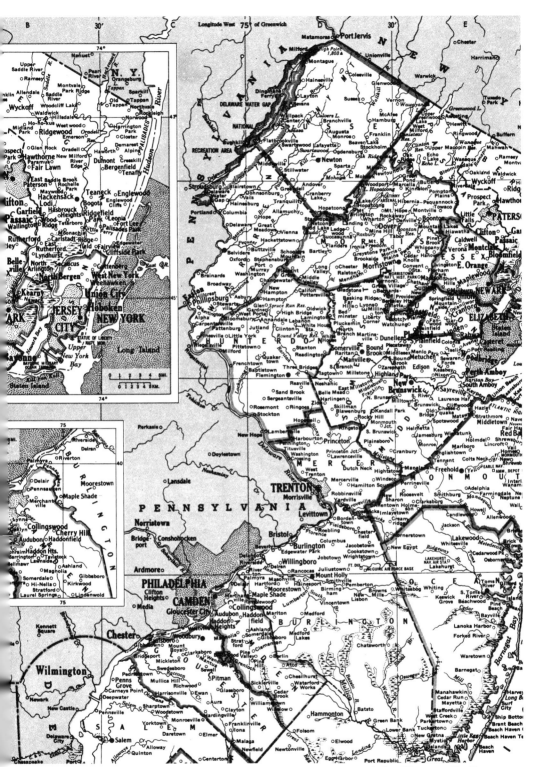

A major portion of the current (1973) New Jersey map prepared for Hammond's *Perspective* series of world atlases. Against a white background, counties are bordered with various colors. Traditional railroads are deleted. Roads and terrain appear on separate, smaller maps. © *Hammond Inc.*

Map of Union County, New Jersey, full-size detail. By Hammond Inc., 1971. One of the best examples of official county road maps issued by the various Boards of Chosen Free-holders. © *Hammond Inc.*

1900's in map artistry. Unlike Rand McNally, Hammond continues to emphasize counties, using solid colors into the early 1960's, but bordering the counties with various colors in the new series of atlases issued since 1966. In this series, Hammond dropped railroads altogether, but shows main highways, topography, and economic features on separate small-scale maps adjacent to the main map. The half-degree grid is there, but no projection is named.

For one's own state, atlases are usually inadequate for mapping facts. They tell a little less about many more areas of the world, and could not do differently without prohibitive cost and, for most users, irrelevancy.

MAPS OF COUNTIES

The county atlases of the beginning of the twentieth century lost their appeal. Too expensive for updating, they passed out of print, and, except for the special interest atlases of counties, there were no more until the middle of the century. Sheet maps of counties came back into style with the advent of road maps. Since the 1930's, every county in New Jersey has had a road map to issue to the public upon request. These vary from excellent to poor, from a modest charge to free, from government-made to privately contracted.

Several counties—Passaic, Bergen, Essex, Hudson and Middlesex —use slightly modified full-color versions of the commercial Hagstrom street maps of the counties. Some of the poorer counties issue uncolored, rather crude maps which are difficult to follow and lack most street names.

At or near the top of the list of the most attractive and precise official county maps are two designed—perhaps coincidentally—by the New Jersey-based map firms: Morris County is shown at 0.85 miles/inch in several colors by General Drafting Co., and Union County is prepared multicolor at 2,000 feet/inch by Hammond. General Drafting also prepares neat official maps of Sussex, Warren, Hunterdon, and Atlantic Counties, but with fewer colors and details.

For $1.50 per map, the traveler can get a well-labeled Hagstrom street map of each county in the New York metropolitan area, as far out as Morris, Somerset, Mercer, and Ocean Counties. At higher prices, Hagstrom enlarges most of these maps and issues them in booklet form as atlases. For $1.50 or less, there are street maps of Camden, Hunterdon, and Sussex Counties and of the more populous portions of Burlington County, drawn by other firms. Unlike the large county maps of the nineteenth century, those of the mid-twentieth are revised every one to ten years, and are designed to be discarded and replaced.

For Warren, Gloucester, and Atlantic Counties and points south, the customer cannot find county maps with completely labeled streets at budget prices, although the streets of some of the larger towns are named on insets. If the traveler wants a detailed street map of all twenty-one counties, complete with street names, he must pay $152.50 per county for an oilcloth wall map of each, sold by Hearne Bros. of Detroit.

MAPS OF TOWNS

During the late nineteenth and early twentieth centuries, finely drawn, large-scale maps of the major cities of New Jersey were published as wall maps. Some of the townships were also honored in this way. Large and small towns were detailed as insets or as separate maps in the state and county atlases of the period.[32] Commercial publishers still produce separate maps of the larger cities, but individual maps of other communities are often unavailable at book or stationery shops.

Many municipalities issue their own maps, which serve as more up-to-date base maps. If counties have a variety of official maps, official municipal maps are of almost endless types. At the low end are the many municipalities, especially rural townships, which have no street maps available to the public at all, or have only zoning or other maps which are not for general purposes.

At the pleasant end of the spectrum are attractive public relations products in color, such as Sparta Township's official map. In between are black and white professional works, usually prepared by the municipal engineer's office, or by other engineering firms, with street width to scale and landmarks located and identified. One

Morris County borough, for example, issues a fairly complete map
showing all churches, as well as schools and public buildings. The
borough map even went so far as to stress that two churches, listed
last, were "colored." There were apparently no objections to this
symbol of inferior classification for some twenty years, until a new
local resident persuaded the borough engineer to remove the unen-
lightened racial notation in 1961.

Finances and foresightedness generally determine the municipal
mapping stance, and New Jersey's 567 "children" are of all varieties.
For legal purposes, tax and zoning maps are usually prepared with
the greatest care and the largest scale, but often are practically
limited to office inspection.

Much poorer in quality are many of the single-line street maps
prepared for free distribution by real estate offices and other commercial outlets. But not necessarily: Hammond Inc. has prepared
several local street maps, covering communities or regions in north
and south Jersey, which meet every qualification for neatness and
legibility, although often in only two colors. The merchants who
issue these can be proud of them.

MISCELLANEOUS MAPS

The listing of all New Jersey maps is not the purpose of this
book. The only study which has attempted this (but even then omitting all maps drawn earlier than 1800) is a monumental work of
1,540 typewritten pages and unpublished. Painstakingly prepared by
Agnes B. Grametbaur on a grant while she was working at Rutgers
over twenty years ago, it has not been updated since 1949. It is an
annotated bibliography in which numerous pages are devoted to
listing the individual topographic quadrangles and the various
municipal maps. It is thoroughly indexed by place, publisher and
surveyor.[33]

Since there are several other types of maps which we have not
mentioned, it would be well to point out some of them in passing.

There are two outline maps of New Jersey, showing only counties
and municipalities in black and white. They are useful base maps
for a variety of purposes. One has been issued by the U.S. Census

Bureau at a scale of 4 miles/inch, revised for each decennial census since 1940. The other is issued by the New Jersey Division of State and Regional Planning at various scales. Both have minor errors, some overlooked through many updatings. The federal map is somewhat out of shape.

When features of the base map are replaced with pictures, popular and attractive pictorial maps result. Geological and soil maps are usually superimposed on New Jersey Topographical Atlas Sheets, which were originally drawn to aid the geological survey. Barker [34] lists specialized maps available from various governmental agencies, as of 1965, while a regularly revised list of "Maps and Publications," free from the State Bureau of Geology and Topography, describes maps currently for sale by the Bureau.

Maps on which population density, rainfall, consumer preferences, and the like are shown are really charts using as a base an appealing map rather than a more prosaic bar chart or a circular pie. New Jersey's Department of Community Affairs, Division of State and Regional Planning (P.O. Box 1978, Trenton 08625) issues a free list of their various maps, including this type.

Reconstructed historical maps serve a different purpose. The original maps of two or three hundred years ago were drawn by men who were working from limited surveys and who often knew little of the boundaries and roads of the day. A modern historian can weigh old and new information to try to reconstruct as accurately as possible a map of the past. For reconstructed maps with dates later than Gordon's map of 1828, the modern cartographer has a rather minor advantage. Before 1828, the maps are so inaccurate or incomplete that he has a fertile field. The challenge is in separating the correct from the incorrect.

This author, concentrating on civil boundaries in an earlier published study, assembled apparently for the first time enough information to make possible fairly accurate boundary reconstructions for all of the pre-1828 period, as well as for the better-mapped decades since. Thus he constructed the only known township map of the young state for the Revolutionary era.[35]

High on the list of popular reconstructed (as well as original) maps of parts of New Jersey are those showing army marches and maneuvers taking place during the Revolution, since many battles and encampments occurred in Jersey. Several books, past and present, dwell on this phase of New Jersey history. The Philip Freneau Press of Monmouth Beach, N.J., has been specializing in Revolutionary history of the state, with almost a dozen books in print or in preparation. This author has chosen not to compete with Revolutionary buffs in covering this action-filled specialty, but to work instead on the less discussed but more extensive maps of New Jersey's broader history.

Reconstructed road maps would be at least as useful, but only limited work has been (or perhaps can be) done in this area. The actual movement of shore lines and river beds is another area for more research. Many existing reconstructed maps are also seriously in error due to limitations of resource material.

A different kind of transportation map is the trail map. Those who even find driving the back roads too close to civilization take to narrow foot trails, bridle paths, and old woods roads which are maintained by state park and state forest personnel, or by private hiking clubs. Northwest Jersey, especially, has many miles of trails, of which only the Appalachian Trail is shown on highway maps. The rest are shown to various extents on state park maps, in the *New York Walk Book*,[36] on U.S. Geological Survey topographic quadrangles, and especially on Hikers Region Maps.

The latter, a set of several dozen 8½" by 11" or 11" by 17" sheets in black and white, were prepared and updated over a thirty-year period by William Hoeferlin of New York City. After working for Rand McNally in the 1920's, he set out on his own to publish maps and trail guides. An inveterate hiker, he died at seventy-two in 1970, following a heart attack suffered while leading yet another hike. The presence of contour lines without color and imperfect lettering somewhat limit legibility of his maps, but the information and the dedication are there. The maps, which cover hiking areas in the New York metropolitan area, are undergoing complete revision by others.

WHAT TO LOOK FOR IN MODERN MAPS

With the constant output of new maps, the map lover will be attracted to some and will feel indifferent to others, or even repelled. Aside from choosing maps (preferably brightly colored ones) to cover the areas which interest him, what are some of the subtle qualities to look for?

It is probably agreed that the most important requirement of a map is that it be accurate. On further consideration, it is realized that perfect accuracy can be a handicap. Plastic relief maps without any vertical exaggeration would be too flat. Highways shown on a state highway map at their true-scale width would be too thin to follow easily. A state map with all the local roads would be too cluttered for most travelers to use.

Maps must be made with the user in mind. In view of the difficulty of assembling the information, one should not be too critical of a road map ten years behind on minor county boundary changes, if it is up to date on the construction status of major roads. It is carrying out its intended purpose.

A number of street maps are drawn with double-line streets, the names being printed between the lines. The city blocks are smaller than they should be, but this is done deliberately to make the names more legible. A less defensible characteristic of some street maps is the map maker's habit of including all the paper streets on his map because they are on the municipal source map (for legal reasons), even though they are not cut through, and in some cases never will be. The traveler often finds out only when he is trying to take a fictitious shortcut.

The recent trend on some road maps to make major highways so prominent, wide, and smooth that the back roads look almost like foot trails seems to the author to be an unwarranted inaccuracy which only encourages highway congestion. It discourages the use of back roads which are sometimes better surfaced than main roads.

The map user can usually judge legibility more easily than accuracy. Illegibility can make the accuracy useless. For example, on some single-line street maps the street names overlap the side streets so that the user can't tell whether there is an intersection. Poor lettering, uneven printing and excess cluttering seriously detract from otherwise useful maps. One especially ugly compilation of reprinted New Jersey street maps ends up with many different map styles and scales (none identified). The compiler also shows an intense aversion to blank space and fills it all with advertisements.

All the accuracy and legibility on a map will not help if the map is unavailable or unknown to the user. While commercial map makers have their wares available at gasoline service stations, drugstores, or bookstores, government publications, including maps, can be bought from few sources. There are only ten outlets in New Jersey for selling U.S. topographic maps. Several are open only during normal office hours. State topographic maps are sold only at the Bureau of Geology and Topography in Trenton on weekdays. Municipal street maps are usually available only at the particular municipal building, on weekdays. Ordering by mail requires both faith in the suitability of the item, often sight unseen, and knowledge of its existence by happening to hear of the source.

For some areas, the most ardent map seeker will be frustrated. The metropolitan areas of New Jersey are well mapped with topographic maps, county street maps, municipal maps, and large-scale road maps. With the rural areas, it is a different story. As mentioned earlier, for several counties there are no detailed street maps popularly available. The same is true of several towns and townships. Maps cost money to prepare, but in many cases the missing link is not the customer, but a small and interested map maker who is not too busy with the more popular map subjects.

These needs are not unique to Jersey, but on the other hand its long-time existence and high population density have not made it immune to them. For its small size, it has probably the greatest range of terrain, towns, and travel of any state. New Jersey map makers have not exhausted their field. We'll be looking for more of their treasures.

State and County Maps and Atlases Before 1910

Based on lists of existing copies and personal observations, this listing includes state maps issued prior to the Topographic Survey of 1877–88 which were equal or superior to their predecessors, all state atlases (none has been issued since 1905), general sheet maps of counties published before 1910 as scales of 2 miles/inch or larger, and general county atlases prior to 1910. All Colton maps listed are road maps. Most but not all other county maps identify property owners. "A" after the date indicates "atlas." Others are sheet maps.[1]

Date	Author or Surveyor	Publisher & Place	Scale miles/inch
		New Jersey Sheet Maps	
ca. 1664	—	John Seller, London	
ca. 1677	—	John Seller, London	
ca. 1700	John Worlidge	John Thornton, London	9½
1777, '78	Bernard Ratzer, Gerard Bancker, et al.	William Faden, London	6⅔
1812	—	William Watson, Gloucester Co.	4
1828, '33, '50	Thomas Gordon	H. S. Tanner, Phila.	3
1854	Robert E. Hornor (& Gordon)	H. S. Tanner, Phila.	3
1860	Wm. Kitchell & G. M. Hopkins	H. G. Bond, Phila.	2½
1868	G. M. Hopkins & G. H. Cook	State of N.J.	2

Date	Author or Surveyor	Publisher & Place	Scale miles/inch
		New Jersey Atlases	
1872A	F. W. Beers	Beers, Comstock & Cline, N.Y.	2 (for counties)
1873A	G. M. Hopkins	G. M. Hopkins, Phila.	4 (for counties)
ca. 1889A	C. C. Vermeule	N.J. Geological Survey	1
1905A	A. L. Westgard	Survey Map Co., N.Y.	4/7 to 2 (for counties)
		Atlantic County	
1872	F. W. Beers	Beers, Comstock & Cline, N.Y.	5/8
		Bergen County	
1861 (incl. Passaic)	G. M. Hopkins	G. H. Corey, Phila.	2/3
1874	A. M. Clay	Clay, N.Y.	2/3
1876A	A. H. Walker	C. C. Pease, Reading, Pa.	300'–2150'
1894	G. W. & C. B. Colton & Co.	Colton, N.Y.	1¼
1896	G. W. & C. B. Colton & Co.	Colton, N.Y.	1½
1902	E. Robinson & Co.	Robinson, N.Y.	2000'
1909	Herbert B. Potter	Robt. A. Welcke, N.Y.	0.39
		Burlington County	
1849	J. W. Otley & R. Whiteford	Smith & Wistar, Phila.	0.84
1858, '59	Wm. Parry, Geo. Sykes & F. W. Earl	R. K. Kuhn & J. D. Janney	0.80
1876A, '78A	J. D. Scott	Scott, Phila.	

Date	Author or Surveyor	Publisher & Place	Scale miles/inch

Camden County

Date	Author or Surveyor	Publisher & Place	Scale
1846	John Clement, Jr.	Clement, Camden	1
1856, '57	—	R. L. Barnes, Phila., & Lloyd Vanderveer, Camden	⅔

Cape May County

Date	Author or Surveyor	Publisher & Place	Scale
1872	F. W. Beers	Beers, Comstock, & Cline, N.Y.	⅝

Cumberland County

Date	Author or Surveyor	Publisher & Place	Scale
1862	S. N. & F. W. Beers, L. B. Lake & C. S. Warner	A. Pomeroy, Phila.	0.62
1876A	D. J. Stewart	D. J. Stewart, Phila.	not given

Essex County

Date	Author or Surveyor	Publisher & Place	Scale
1850	J. C. Sidney	Hiram A. Belding, Newark	0.51
1859	H. F. Walling	Baker & Tilden, N.Y.	0.32
1874	Matthew Hughes	Hughes, Orange, N.J.	0.23
1877	W. A. Mirick	J. S. Schaeffer	0.58
1881A	Roger H. Pidgeon	E. Robinson, N.Y.	200'–2400'
1889	F. N. Moffatt	F. N. Moffatt & Co.	not given
1889	Scarlett & Scarlett	F. N. Moffatt & Co.	not given
1890, '93	—	J. H. Baldwin, Orange, N.J.	0.40
1890	E. Robinson	Robinson, N.Y.	2000'
1890A	E. Robinson	Robinson, N.Y.	200'–2000'
1898 (incl. Union)	—	Colton, Ohman & Co., N.Y.	⅘
1906A	Ellis Kiser	A. H. Mueller, Phila.	200'–1600'

Date	Author or Surveyor	Publisher & Place	Scale miles/inch
		Gloucester County	
1849 (incl. Salem)	Alexr. C. Stansbie, James Keily, & Saml. M. Rea	Smith & Wistar, Phila.	0.82
1876A, '77A (incl. Salem)	Everts & Stewart	Everts & Stewart, Phila.	not given
		Hudson County	
1767 (while in Bergen)	—	(manuscript)[2]	¼
1860 (incl. N.Y. area)	—	J. H. Higginson, N.Y.	1
1873A	G. M. Hopkins —	Hopkins, Phila. (combined atlas of N.J. and Hudson Co.)	150′–400′
1880A	Spielmann & Brush	Spielmann & Brush, Hoboken	1000′
1909A	—	G. M. Hopkins Co., Phila.	
1910	—	Interstate Map Co., Newark	1000′
		Hunterdon County	
1851	Samuel C. Cornell	Lloyd Vanderveer & S. C. Cornell	⅔
1873A	F. W. Beers	Beers, Comstock & Cline, N.Y.	264′–3300′
1902	Pugh & Downing	Irving C. Hicks, Phila.	⅔
		Mercer County	
1849	J. W. Otley & J. Keily	Lloyd Vanderveer, Camden	⅔
1875A	Everts & Stewart	Everts & Stewart, Phila.	
1903	Pugh & Downing	Irving C. Hicks, Phila.	½
1905	—	A. H. Mueller, & Co., Phila.	½
		Middlesex County	
(1766)	I. Hills & Az. Dunham	(manuscript)	⅝

Date	Author or Surveyor	Publisher & Place	Scale miles/inch
	Middlesex County (Cont.)		
1781	I. Hills	(manuscript)	1
1850	J. W. Otley & J. Keily	Lloyd Vanderveer, Camden	0.68
1861	H. F. Walling	Smith, Gallup & Co.	0.47
1876A	Everts & Stewart	Everts & Stewart, Phila.	300′–2640′ & unmarked
	Monmouth County		
1781	I. Hills	(manuscript, drawn for Gen. Clinton)	1
1851	Jesse Lightfoot	J. B. Shields, Middletown Point, N.J.	⅔
1860, '61	S. N. & F. W. Beers, & H. F. Walling	Smith, Gallup, & Holt, N.Y.	⅝
1873A	F. W. Beers	Beers, Comstock & Cline, N.Y.	264′–4150′
1889A	Chester Wolverton & Forsey Breou	Chester Wolverton, N.Y.	150′–2112′
1889, '94	G. W. & C. B. Colton & Co.	Colton, N.Y.	⅘
	Morris County		
1853	J. Lightfoot & Saml. Geil	J. B. Shields, Morristown, N.J.	⅔
1868A	F. W. Beers	F. W. Beers, A. D. Ellis & G. G. Soule, N.Y.	330′–2640′
1887A	E. Robinson	Robinson, N.Y.	300′–2640′
	Ocean County		
1781 (part of Monmouth Co., q.v.)			
1872	F. W. Beers	Beers, Comstock & Cline, N.Y.	⅝
	Passaic County		
1861 (see Bergen)			
1877A	—	E. B. Hyde & Co., N.Y.	230′–2800′
1892, '95	G. W. & C. B. Colton & Co.	Colton, N.Y.	1½

Date	Author or Surveyor	Publisher & Place	Scale miles/inch

Salem County

1849 (see Gloucester)
1876A, '77A (see Gloucester)

Somerset County

Date	Author or Surveyor	Publisher & Place	Scale miles/inch
(1766)	I. Hills & Benj. Morgan	(manuscript)	⅝
1781	I. Hills	(manuscript)	1
1850	J. W. Otley & J. Keily	Lloyd Vanderveer, Camden	⅔
1850	Otley, Vanderveer & Keily	Lloyd Vanderveer, Camden	⅔
1873A	F. W. Beers	Beers, Comstock & Cline, N.Y.	300'–3300'

Sussex County

Date	Author or Surveyor	Publisher & Place	Scale miles/inch
1860	G. M. Hopkins	Carlos Allen, Phila.	⅔
1894	G. W. & C. B. Colton & Co.	Colton, N.Y.	1½

Union County

Date	Author or Surveyor	Publisher & Place	Scale miles/inch
1850 (part of Essex Co., q.v.)			
1862	Ernest L. Meyer & P. Witzel		⅓
1882A	E. Robinson & R. H. Pidgeon	E. Robinson, N.Y.	200'–1500'
1898 (see Essex)			
1903	J. L. Bauer	Robert A. Welcke, N.Y.	2500'
1906A	Jacob L. Bauer	E. Robinson, N.Y.	200'–1800'

Warren County

Date	Author or Surveyor	Publisher & Place	Scale miles/inch
1852	D. McCarty		¾
1860, '61	H. F. Walling & G. M. Hopkins	Smith, Gallup & Co., N.Y.	⅔
1874A	F. W. Beers	F. W. Beers & Co., N.Y.	330'–3300'

APPENDIX B

Current County Maps and Atlases

Dates of maps are not listed here because several are not given on the map, and nearly all are revised regularly. Most of the commercial sheet maps cost $1.50 each, and are available at bookstores and stationery shops. Hearne Bros. maps, on oilcloth only, cost $152.50 each from special distributors. Maps issued by counties are generally free, but some cost up to $1.00. They may be obtained by writing to the Board of Chosen Freeholders at the respective county seats. Atlases, which on this list are sectionalized direct enlargements of the sheet maps, cost up to $6.95 each at bookstores.

Type: S: All streets shown and named.
M: All streets shown; only main streets named.
N: All streets shown; none named.
R: Only main streets shown and named.
T: Only main streets shown; none named.
A: Atlas; all streets shown and named.
*: Has detailed enlarged insets of one or more towns.

Type	Map Maker	Publisher	Approx. Scale Feet/Inch
		Atlantic	
R	General Drafting Co.	County	8,800
S	Hearne Bros.	Hearne, Detroit	2,300
		Bergen	
S	Hagstrom Co.	County	3,330
S	Hagstrom Co.	Hagstrom, N.Y.	3,330
A	Hagstrom Co.	Hagstrom, N.Y.	2,200
S	Hearne Bros.	Hearne, Detroit	1,760
		Burlington	
T	General Drafting Co.	County	11,600
S	Hearne Bros.	Hearne, Detroit	2,200
S (part)	C. W. Dansbury	Dansbury, Trenton	3,200

			Approx. Scale
Type	Map Maker	Publisher	Feet/Inch

Camden

S	Arrow Maps, Inc.	County	3,400
S	Hearne Bros.	Hearne, Detroit	2,500
S (part)	Hammond Inc.	Hammond, Maplewood	2,000

Cape May

T	L. E. Peterson	County	5,280
R* (part)	Laws Printing Industries	Cape May Co. Bridge Commission	11,000
S	Hearne Bros.	Hearne, Detroit	2,300

Cumberland

M*	Co. Engineer	County	10,560
S	Hearne Bros.	Hearne, Detroit	2,200

Essex

S	Hagstrom Co.	County	2,640
S	Hagstrom Co.	Hagstrom, N.Y.	2,640
S	Hearne Bros.	Hearne, Detroit	1,510
A	Hagstrom Co.	Hagstrom, N.Y.	1,800

Gloucester

T*	Co. Engineer	County	5,280
S	Hearne Bros.	Hearne, Detroit	1,920

Hudson

S	Hagstrom Co.	County	2,100
S	Hagstrom Co.	Hagstrom, N.Y.	2,100
S	Hearne Bros.	Hearne, Detroit	1,210

Hunterdon

N	General Drafting Co.	County	7,300
S	Arrow Guide Div. R. L. Polk & Co.	Arrow Guide, Boston	5,600
S	Hearne Bros.	Hearne, Detroit	1,920

	Type	Map Maker	Publisher	Approx. Scale Feet/Inch

Mercer

Type	Map Maker	Publisher	Approx. Scale Feet/Inch
M	Co. Engineer	County	4,000
S	C. W. Dansbury	Dansbury, Trenton	3,100
S*	Hagstrom Co.	Hagstrom, N.Y.	3,900
S	Hearne Bros.	Hearne, Detroit	2,200
A	Hagstrom Co.	Hagstrom, N.Y.	2,300

Middlesex

Type	Map Maker	Publisher	Approx. Scale Feet/Inch
S	Hagstrom Co.	County	3,600
S	Hagstrom Co.	Hagstrom, N.Y.	3,600
S	Hearne Bros.	Hearne, Detroit	1,920
A	Hagstrom Co.	Hagstrom, N.Y.	1,600

Monmouth

Type	Map Maker	Publisher	Approx. Scale Feet/Inch
M	Hagstrom Co.	County Planning Board	8,000
S	Hagstrom Co.	Hagstrom, N.Y.	3,100 & 9,300
S	Hearne Bros.	Hearne, Detroit	2,200
A	Hagstrom Co.	Hagstrom, N.Y.	2,300 to 8,400

Morris

Type	Map Maker	Publisher	Approx. Scale Feet/Inch
M	General Drafting Co.	County	4,465
S*	Hagstrom Co.	Hagstrom, N.Y.	4,000
S	Hearne Bros.	Hearne, Detroit	2,400
A	Hagstrom Co.	Hagstrom, N.Y.	2,900

Ocean

Type	Map Maker	Publisher	Approx. Scale Feet/Inch
T*	Co. Engineer	County	7,040
S	Hagstrom Co.	Hagstrom, N.Y.	3,800
S	Hearne Bros.	Hearne, Detroit	3,000
A	Hagstrom Co.	Hagstrom, N.Y.	3,000 & 4,000

Passaic

Type	Map Maker	Publisher	Approx. Scale Feet/Inch
S*	Hagstrom Co.	County	4,200
S*	Hagstrom Co.	Hagstrom, N.Y.	4,200
S	Hearne Bros.	Hearne, Detroit	2,200
A	Hagstrom Co.	Hagstrom, N.Y.	2,300

Type	Map Maker	Publisher	Approx. Scale Feet/Inch

Salem

Type	Map Maker	Publisher	Feet/Inch
N*	Hagstrom Co.	County	5,280
S	Hearne Bros.	Hearne, Detroit	1,760

Somerset

Type	Map Maker	Publisher	Feet/Inch
S	R. L. Polk Co.	County	3,600
S	Hagstrom Co.	Hagstrom, N.Y.	3,400
S	Hearne Bros.	Hearne, Detroit	1,960

Sussex

Type	Map Maker	Publisher	Feet/Inch
N	General Drafting Co.	County	7,400
S	Arrow Maps, Inc.	Arrow, Boston	4,800
S	Hearne Bros.	Hearne, Detroit	1,960

Union

Type	Map Maker	Publisher	Feet/Inch
S	Hammond Inc.	County	2,000
S	Hagstrom Co.	Hagstrom, N.Y.	2,200
S	Hearne Bros.	Hearne, Detroit	1,460
A	Hagstrom Co.	Hagstrom, N.Y.	2,200

Warren

Type	Map Maker	Publisher	Feet/Inch
N	General Drafting Co.	County	7,000
S	Hearne Bros.	Hearne, Detroit	1,380

APPENDIX C

New Jersey Geological Survey Maps

Current editions of Atlas Sheets 21–36 are available at $4 each postpaid (payable to Treasurer, State of New Jersey) from:

> Division Map & Publication Sales Office
> Bureau of Geology and Topography
> P.O. Box 1889
> Trenton, New Jersey 08625

Some Topographic Name Sheets are still available at $1 each. All other editions of these sheets, of Sheets 1–20 and 37 (being discontinued and to be inserted on Sheet 36), and of other maps issued by the state are available as diazo reproductions at $19 or $22 each for the first copy and $2 for each additional copy. If the reproduction media are already available, the cost is $2 for the first or each additional copy.

Following are listed each of the Atlas Sheets and Topographic Name Sheets issued by the state, with dates of the various editions and index maps. Contour intervals are 10′ or 20′, depending on terrain, except that no contours are shown on Atlas Sheets 18, 20, and 38–42, and Sheet 19 has 50′ or 100′ contour intervals. The scale for Atlas Sheets 1–17 and 21–37 is 1 mile/inch (1:63,360). On Sheets 18–20 and 38, the scale is 5 miles/inch (1:316,800). On Sheets 39–42, the scale is 3.95 miles/inch (1:250,000). The 24 Topographic Name Sheets are drawn to a scale of 2,000 feet/inch (1:24,000) .

New Jersey Geological Survey Atlas Sheets [1]

No.	Title	Editions
1	Kittatinny Valley and Mountain	1886, 1888, 1889, 1890, 1894
2	Southwestern Highlands	1885, 1889, 1890
3	Central Highlands	1884, 1888, 1889, 1898
4	Northeastern Highlands	1884, 1888, 1889
5	Vicinity of Flemington	1887, 1888, 1889
6	The Valley of the Passaic	1885, 1888, 1889, 1900
7	Bergen, Hudson and Essex	1884, 1888, 1889, 1890, 1896

185

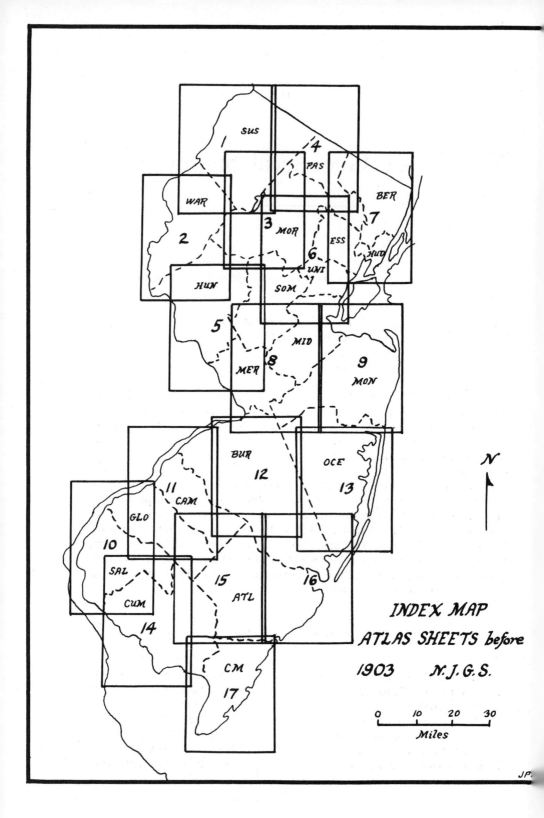

INDEX MAP
ATLAS SHEETS before
1903   N.J.G.S.

New Jersey Geological Survey Atlas Sheets [1] *(Cont.)*

No.	Title	Editions
8	Vicinity of Trenton	1887, 1888, 1889, 1894
9	Monmouth Shore	1886, 1888, 1889, 1902
10	Vicinity of Salem	1887, 1889
11	Vicinity of Camden	1887, 1888, 1889, 1894
12	Vicinity of Mount Holly	1887, 1888, 1889, 1895
13	Vicinity of Barnegat City	1886, 1888, 1889
14	Vicinity of Bridgeton	1887, 1889, 1890
15	Southern Interior	1887, 1889, 1890
16	Egg Harbor and Vicinity	1885, 1888, 1889
17	Peninsula of Cape May	1886, 1888, 1889, 1895
18	The State of New Jersey	1888, 1889
19	New Jersey Relief Map	1888, 1889
20	New Jersey Geological Map	1889, 1890

No.	Region (map not titled)	Editions
21	Kittatinny Valley and Mountain	1906, 1913, 1926, 1946, 1959
22	Eastern Sussex, Western Passaic and Northern Morris	1903, 1910, 1916, 1928, 1933, 1939, 1947, 1960
23	Northern Bergen and Eastern Passaic Counties	1903, 1910, 1916, 1924, 1933, 1947, 1963
24	Southern Warren, Northern Hunterdon and Western Morris Counties	1903, 1912, 1921, 1930, 1936, 1948
25	Morris and Somerset Counties	1906, 1912, 1917, 1928, 1933, 1940, 1954
26	Vicinity of Newark and Jersey City	1903, 1908, 1912, 1916, 1922, 1927, 1932, 1942, 1955
27	Vicinity of Trenton	1903, 1913, 1926, 1930, 1943, 1959
28	Trenton and Eastward	1904, 1912, 1917, 1929, 1932, 1937, 1949, 1957
29	Monmouth Shore	1910, 1914, 1924, 1931, 1938, 1950
30	Parts of Gloucester and Salem Counties	1910, 1926, 1934, 1951
31	Vicinity of Camden to Mount Holly, Hammonton and Elmer	1903, 1913, 1925, 1931, 1942, 1958
32	Southern Burlington County	1903, 1923, 1929, 1934, 1941, 1955, 1970
33	Vicinity of Barnegat Bay	1905, 1913, 1925, 1929, 1934, 1953
34	Southern Salem County and Western Cumberland County	1910, 1927, 1936, 1956
35	Vicinity of Millville	1907, 1917, 1930, 1946, 1963

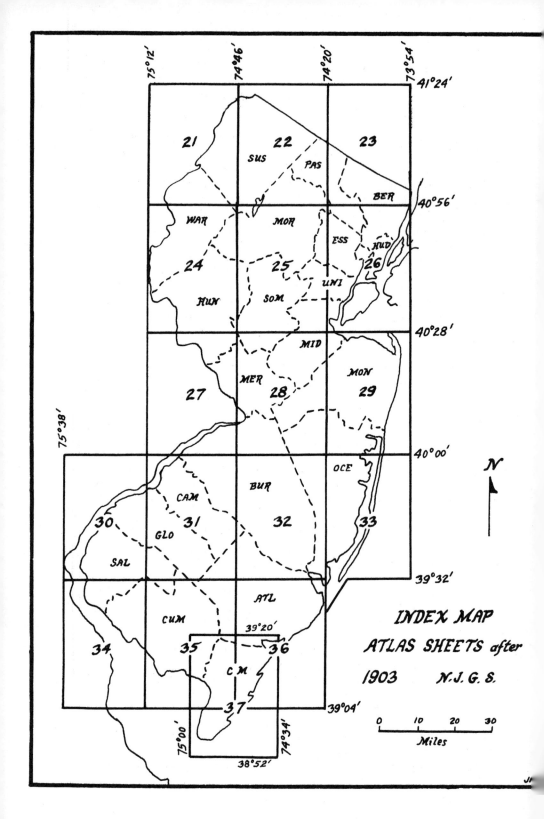

INDEX MAP
ATLAS SHEETS after
1903   N. J. G. S.

0   10   20   30
Miles

New Jersey Geological Survey Atlas Sheets [1] *(Cont.)*

No.	Region *(map not titled)*	Editions
36	Parts of Atlantic and Cape May Counties	1907, 1916, 1934, 1945, 1960
37	Cape May County	1905, 1913, 1929, 1936, 1952
38	New Jersey State Map	1906
39	County and Municipality Map of New Jersey	1915, 1918, 1925, 1932, 1939, 1956
40	Geologic Map of New Jersey	1918, 1931, 1950

No.	Title	Editions
41	Railroad Map of New Jersey	1915
42	Map of New Jersey	1916
	Road Map of New Jersey	1922, 1925, 1933

New Jersey Geological Survey Topographic Name Sheets [2]

Name	Editions
Amboy	1901, 1922, 1940
Atlantic City	1902
Boonton	1904, 1905, 1927, 1932
Camden	1900
Chester	1905, 1915, 1930
Dover-Stanhope	1905, 1916, 1932
Elizabeth	1900, 1912, 1919, 1930
Hackensack	1899, 1914, 1934
Jersey City	1899, 1919, 1928
Long Branch	1901, 1931
Morristown	1902, 1917, 1926, 1939
Mount Holly	1900
Navesink	1901, 1932
Newark	1899, 1908, 1914, 1926, 1937
New Brunswick	1905, 1914, 1928, 1939
New York Bay	1903, 1907, 1942
Paterson	1899, 1912, 1922, 1929
Plainfield	1900, 1916, 1928, 1938
Pluckemin	1905, 1917, 1944
Shark River	1903, 1916
Somerville	1905, 1920, 1944
Taunton	1900
Trenton East	1902
Woodbury	1900

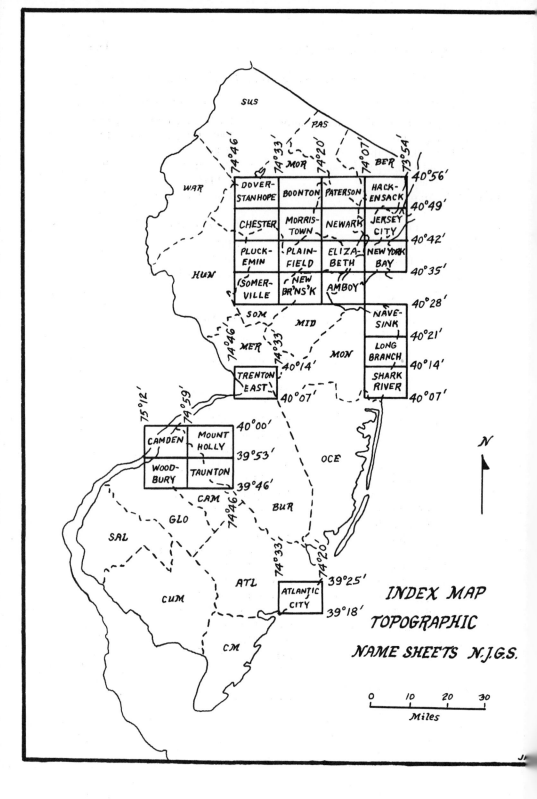

INDEX MAP
TOPOGRAPHIC
NAME SHEETS N.J.G.S.

U.S. Geological Survey Maps
of New Jersey

The U.S. Geological Survey issues current large-scale quadrangles of New Jersey at a scale of 2,000 feet/inch (1:24,000), covering an area 7½ minutes of latitude by 7½ minutes of longitude. The contour interval varies from 5' to 20'. They may be ordered at 75 cents each. The check or money order should be made payable to Geological Survey, and the order placed with

> Washington Distribution Center
> Geological Survey
> 1200 South Eads St.
> Arlington, Va. 22202

To identify quadrangles in ordering, refer to the name of the sheet and state whether the sheet is in the 7½' or the 15' series. On the index map in this book, numbers and letters are given, but they are chosen strictly for use in this book and have no official significance. A free larger-scale (1:500,000) index map is available from the Geological Survey at the above address. Only six different 15' quadrangles were still for sale in 1972, and these will soon be exhausted.

All known editions of Geological Survey and Army Map Service (AMS) quadrangles are listed in the following pages. The Rutgers University Library Special Collections, the Princeton University Library Map Room, and the Morristown Public Library have some of the early editions of the 7½', 15' and 30' series.

Larger areas are covered by the Army Map Service series at a scale of 3.95 miles/inch (1:250,000). Covering 1° Latitude by 2° Longitude, they may be ordered from the Geological Survey at $1.00 each, under the same conditions as above. Contour intervals are 100', occasionally 50'. Refer to AMS names on the index map. Plastic raised-relief forms of three of these 1:250,000 maps (Newark, Scranton, and Hartford) may be purchased for $9.95 each plus handling costs from Hubbard, 2855 Schermer Road, Northbrook, Ill. 60062.

7½-minute Quadrangles

Contour intervals 10′ and 20′. Extent 7½′ Long. by 7½′ Lat. Three series of scales (currently 2,000 ft./inch only).[1]

Editions

Index Map Area	Name of Quadrangle	USGS 1:31,680 2640′/in.	AMS 1:25,000 2083′/in.	USGS 1:24,000 2000′/in.
1	Milford, Pa.			1958
2	Port Jervis South, N.Y.	1943	1943, 1946, 1949	1946
3	Unionville, N.Y.	1943	1943, 1946, 1949	1946, 1969
4	Pine Island, N.Y.		1943, 1946, 1949	1942, 1969
5	Lake Maskenozha, Pa.		1943, 1946	1954
6	Culvers Gap		1943, 1946	1954
7	Branchville		1943, 1946, 1949	1954
8	Hamburg		1943, 1946	1954
9	Wawayanda		1943, 1946	1954
10	Greenwood Lake		1943, 1946	1954
11	Sloatsburg, N.Y.			1955
12	Bushkill, Pa.	1947	1948	1944, 1968
13	Flatbrookville		1943, 1946, 1949	1954
14	Newton West		1943, 1946, 1949	1954
15	Newton East		1943, 1946	1954
16	Franklin		1943, 1946, 1949	1954
17	Newfoundland		1943, 1946, 1949	1954
18	Wanaque		1943, 1948	1954
19	Ramsey	1940, 1945	1947	1955
20	Park Ridge	1939, 1945		1955
21	Nyack, N.Y.	1943	1943, 1947	1957, 1967
22	Stroudsburg, Pa.		1943, 1946	1955, 1968
23	Portland		1943, 1946, 1949	1955
24	Blairstown		1943, 1946, 1949	1955
25	Tranquility		1943, 1946	1954
26	Stanhope		1943, 1946, 1949	1954
27	Dover		1943, 1947	1954
28	Boonton		1943, 1947	1954
29	Pompton Plains		1943, 1947	1955
30	Paterson	1940, 1944		1955
31	Hackensack	1940		1955
32	Yonkers, N.Y.		1943, 1947	1949, 1956, 1966
33	Bangor, Pa.		1943, 1946	1956, 1968
34	Belvidere		1943, 1946, 1949	1955

		Editions		
Index Map Area	*Name of Quadrangle*	*USGS 1:31,680 2640'/in.*	*AMS 1:25,000 2083'/in.*	*USGS 1:24,000 2000'/in.*
35	Washington		1943, 1946, 1949	1954
36	Hackettstown		1943, 1946, 1949	1953
37	Chester		1943, 1946	1954
38	Mendham		1943, 1947	1954
39	Morristown		1943, 1947	1949, 1954
40	Caldwell		1943, 1947	1949, 1954
41	Orange		1943, 1947	1949, 1955
42	Weehawken	1940	1947	1955, 1967
43	Central Park, N.Y.		1943, 1947	1949, 1956
44	Easton, Pa.		1942, 1946, 1949	1956, 1968
45	Bloomsbury		1942, 1946, 1949	1955
46	High Bridge		1942, 1946, 1949	1955
47	Califon		1942, 1946, 1949	1954
48	Gladstone		1942, 1946, 1949	1954
49	Bernardsville		1943, 1947	1949, 1954
50	Chatham		1943, 1947	1949, 1955
51	Roselle		1943, 1947	1949, 1955
52	Elizabeth		1943, 1947	1949, 1955, 1967
53	Jersey City		1943, 1947	1949, 1955, 1967
54	Riegelsville		1942, 1946	1956, 1968
55	Frenchtown		1942, 1946, 1949	1955
56	Pittstown (or Cakepoulin Creek—AMS name)		1942, 1946	1955
57	Flemington		1942, 1946	1954
58	Raritan		1942, 1946, 1949	1955
59	Bound Brook		1943, 1947	1955
60	Plainfield		1943, 1947	1949, 1955
61	Perth Amboy		1943, 1947	1949, 1956
62	Arthur Kill		1943, 1947	1949, 1955, 1966
63	Lumberville		1942, 1946	1955, 1968
64	Stockton		1942, 1946	1954
65	Hopewell		1942, 1946	1954
66	Rocky Hill		1942, 1946	1954
67	Monmouth Junction		1944, 1947	1954
68	New Brunswick	1942		1954
69	South Amboy	1941	1943, 1947	1954
70	Keyport		1943, 1947	1949, 1954

Editions

Index Map Area	Name of Quadrangle	USGS 1:31,680 2640'/in.	AMS 1:25,000 2083'/in.	USGS 1:24,000 2000'/in.
71	Sandy Hook*		1943, 1947	1950, 1954
72	Lambertville		1942, 1946, 1949	1953, 1968
73	Pennington		1942, 1946, 1949	1954
74	Princeton		1942, 1946, 1949	1954
75	Hightstown		1944, 1947	1954
76	Jamesburg		1944, 1947	1953
77	Freehold		1943, 1947	1953
78	Marlboro		1943, 1947	1954
79	Long Branch*		1944, 1947	1949, 1954
80	Trenton West		1944, 1947	1950, 1955
81	Trenton East		1944, 1947, 1949	1949, 1957
82	Allentown		1944, 1947, 1949	1949, 1957
83	Roosevelt		1944, 1947, 1948	1949, 1957
84	Adelphia		1944, 1947, 1948	1949, 1957
85	Farmingdale		1943, 1947	1954
86	Asbury Park*		1942, 1943, 1947	1954
87	Frankford, Pa.			1950, 1967
88	Beverly		1944, 1947	1950, 1955, 1966
89	Bristol, Pa.		1944, 1947	1950, 1955
90	Columbus		1944, 1947, 1949	1949, 1957
91	New Egypt		1944, 1947, 1949	1949, 1957
92	Cassville		1944, 1947, 1949	1949, 1957
93	Lakehurst		1944, 1947, 1949	1949, 1957
94	Lakewood		1944, 1947	1947, 1954
95	Point Pleasant		1942, 1947	1953
96	Philadelphia, Pa.			1949, 1967
97	Camden			1949, 1967
98	Moorestown			1953, 1966
99	Mt. Holly			1953, 1967
100	Pemberton			1949, 1957
101	Browns Mills			1949, 1957
102	Whiting			1949, 1957
103	Keswick Grove			1949, 1957
104	Toms River			1953
105	Seaside Park			1953
106	Marcus Hook, Pa.	1941, 1948		1953, 1967
107	Bridgeport	1941, 1944	1949	1953, 1967
108	Woodbury			1949, 1967

* Quadrangle extends somewhat beyond 7½' width to complete the coastline.

		Editions		
Index		*USGS*	*AMS*	*USGS*
Map	*Name of*	*1:31,680*	*1:25,000*	*1:24,000*
Area	*Quadrangle*	*2640'/in.*	*2083'/in.*	*2000'/in.*
109	Runnemede			1952, 1967
110	Clementon			1953, 1967
111	Medford Lakes			1953, 1967
112	Indian Mills			1949, 1957
113	Chatsworth			1947, 1957
114	Woodmansie			1949, 1957
115	Brookville			1949, 1957
116	Forked River			1953
117	Barnegat Light			1953
118	Wilmington South			1948, 1967
119	Penns Grove			1948, 1967
120	Woodstown			1955, 1967
121	Pitman West			1953, 1967
122	Pitman East			1953, 1966
123	Williamstown			1953, 1966
124	Hammonton			1953, 1966
125	Atsion			1953
126	Jenkins			1956
127	Oswego Lake			1955
128	West Creek			1951
129	Ship Bottom			1952
130	Long Beach NE			1951
131	Delaware City, Del.			1948
132	Salem			1948
133	Alloway			1955
134	Elmer			1953
135	Newfield			1953
136	Buena			1953
137	Newtonville			1953
138	Egg Harbor City			1956
139	Green Bank			1956
140	New Gretna			1951
141	Tuckerton			1952
142	Beach Haven			1951
143	Taylors Bridge, Del.			1948
144	Canton			1949
145	Shiloh			1949
146	Bridgeton			1953
147	Millville			1953
148	Five Points			1956

		Editions		
Index		USGS	AMS	USGS
Map	*Name of*	*1:31,680*	*1:25,000*	*1:24,000*
Area	*Quadrangle*	*2640'/in.*	*2083'/in.*	*2000'/in.*
149	Dorothy			1956
150	Mays Landing			1955
151	Pleasantville			1952
152	Oceanville			1952
153	Brigantine Inlet			1952
154	Bombay Hook, Del.			1949, 1956
155	Ben Davis Point			1949, 1956
156	Cedarville			1956
157	Dividing Creek			1956
158	Port Elizabeth			1956
159	Tuckahoe			1956
160	Marmora			1952
161	Ocean City			1952
162	Atlantic City			1952
163	Fortescue			1956
164	Port Norris			1956
165	Heislerville			1957
166	Woodbine			1958
167	Sea Isle City			1952
168	Rio Grande		1944	1956
169	Stone Harbor		1944	1950, 1955
170	Avalon			1953
171	Cape May		1944	1950, 1954
172	Wildwood		1944	1950, 1955

15-minute Quadrangles

Contour intervals 10' and 20'. Extent 15' Long. by 15' Lat. Two series of scales. Reprint dates are not listed.[1]

		Editions	
Index		USGS	AMS
Map	*Name of*	*1:62,500*	*1:50,000*
Area	*Quadrangle*	*0.99 mi./in.*	*0.79 mi./in.*
A	Milford, Pa.	1915	1944, 1946, 1947
B	Port Jervis, N.Y.	1908	
C	Goshen, N.Y.	1908	
D	Bushkill, Pa.	(never issued)	
E	Wallpack *or* Dingman's Ferry	1891, 1893, 1942, 1954	

Editions

Index Map Area	Name of Quadrangle	USGS 1:62,500 0.99 mi/in.	AMS 1:50,000 0.79 mi/in.
F	Franklin Furnace	1888, 1894, 1897, 1903	
G	Greenwood Lake	1891, 1893, 1903, 1910	
H	Ramapo, N.Y.	1891, 1893, 1910, 1938	
J	Tarrytown, N.Y.	1892, 1893, 1902	
K	Delaware Water Gap	1891, 1893, 1942	
L	Hackettstown	1888, 1894, 1898, 1905	
M	Lake Hopatcong	1888, 1894, 1898, 1905	
N	Morristown	1888, 1894, 1898, 1906	
P	Paterson	1892, 1898, 1900, 1903	
Q	Harlem, N.Y.	1891, 1898, 1900	
R	Easton, Pa.	1890, 1891, 1932	
S	High Bridge	1890, 1898, 1905	
T	Somerville	1891, 1893, 1898, 1905	
U	Plainfield	1888, 1893, 1898, 1905	
V	Staten Island, N.Y.	1898, 1900	
X	Doylestown, Pa.	1891	
Y	Lambertville	1890, 1891, 1894, 1906	
Z	Princeton	1888, 1894, 1906	
AA	New Brunswick	1888, 1893, 1901	
AB	Sandy Hook	1888, 1893, 1901	
AC	Germantown, Pa.	1890, 1893, 1896, 1899	
AD	Burlington	1890, 1893, 1906	
AE	Bordentown	1888, 1893, 1906, 1948	
AF	Cassville (or Lakehurst—AMS)	1888, 1894, 1900, 1948	
AG	Asbury Park	1888, 1893, 1901	
AH	Chester, Pa.	1896, 1898	
AJ	Philadelphia, Pa.	1891, 1896, 1898	1943, 1946
AK	Mount Holly	1888, 1894, 1898	
AL	Pemberton	1888, 1894, 1898, 1949	
AM	Whiting	1888, 1949	
AN	Barnegat (or Toms River—AMS)	1888, 1893, 1898, 1940 1949*	1941, 1946, 1948
AP	Wilmington, Del.	1906	
AQ	Salem	1890, 1898, 1949*	1941, 1946, 1948
AR	Glassboro	1890, 1898, 1949*	1942, 1946, 1948
AS	Hammonton	1890, 1894, 1898, 1948*	1942, 1946, 1948

* AMS sheet at 1:62,500, reprinted by USGS.

Editions

Index Map Area	Name of Quadrangle	USGS 1:62,500 0.99 mi/in.	AMS 1:50,000 0.79 mi/in.
AT	Mullica (or Egg Harbor—AMS)	1890, 1894, 1898	1942, 1946, 1948
AU	Little Egg Harbor (or Tuckerton—AMS)	1888, 1893, 1940	1942, 1946, 1948
AV	Long Beach	1888, 1893, 1941, 1948*	1941, 1946, 1948
AW	Smyrna, Del.	1931	
AX	Shiloh (or Bay Side—AMS)	1890, 1894, 1931	
AY	Bridgeton	1890, 1894, 1948*	1942, 1946, 1948
AZ	Tuckahoe	1890, 1893	1941, 1946, 1948
BA	Great Egg Harbor (or Pleasantville—AMS)	1890, 1893, 1940, 1948*	1942, 1946, 1948
BB	Atlantic City	1887, 1894	1941, 1946, 1948
BC	Maurice Cove (or Port Norris—AMS)	1890, 1891, 1940	1941, 1946, 1948
BD	Dennisville	1884, 1894, 1940	1941, 1946, 1948
BE	Sea Isle (or Sea Isle City—AMS)	1888, 1894, 1940	1941, 1946, 1948
BF	Cape May	1888, 1893	

30-minute Quadrangles

Contour intervals 10′ and 20′. Extent 30′ Long. by 30′ Lat. USGS quadrangle, scale 1:125,000 (1.97 miles/inch).

Index Map Area	Name of Quadrangle	Edition
L, M, S, T	Raritan	1905
N, P, U, V	Passaic	1905
Y, Z, AD, AE	Trenton	1907
AA, AB, AF, AG	Navesink	1902
AH, AJ, AQ, AR	Camden	1901
AK, AL, AS, AT	Rancocas	1900
. . , AW, . . , . .	Dover, Del.	1906
AX, AY, . . , BC	Vineland	1899

* AMS sheet at 1:62,500, reprinted by USGS.

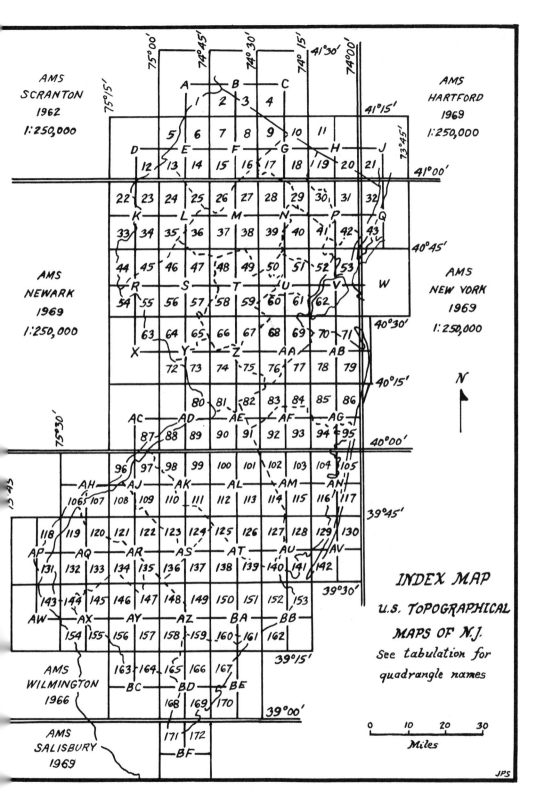

AMS
SCRANTON
1962
1:250,000

AMS
HARTFORD
1969
1:250,000

AMS
NEWARK
1969
1:250,000

AMS
NEW YORK
1969
1:250,000

N

INDEX MAP
U.S. TOPOGRAPHICAL
MAPS OF N.J.
See tabulation for
quadrangle names

AMS
WILMINGTON
1966

AMS
SALISBURY
1969

0   10   20   30
Miles

JPS

199

APPENDIX E

New Jersey State Geologists and Topographers

State Geologists

Henry D. Rogers	1835–1840
William Kitchell	1854–1856
George H. Cook	1864–1889
John C. Smock	1890–1901
Henry B. Kümmel	1901–1937
Meredith E. Johnson	1937–1958
Kemble Widmer	1958–

Topographers or Topographic Engineers [1]

Egbert L. Viele	1854–1856
G. M. Hopkins	1865–1866
Edward A. Bowser	1869–1874
George W. Howell	1871, 1876–1879
James K. Barton	1874–1875
C. C. Vermeule	1878–1895, 1897–1918 (consultant)
Loren P. Plummer	1922–1942
W. Earl Rockford	1942–1943
Robert G. Blanchard	1943–1956
Marvin Gruss	1957–1959
Stanley P. Fisher	1959–1960 (temporary)
Harold Barker, Jr.	1960–1971
George Halasi-kun	1972–

APPENDIX F

Surveyors General of East and West Jersey Proprietors

West New Jersey [1]

Andrew Robeson (Robinson)	1688–1694
Thomas Gardiner	1694–1718
James Alexander	1718–1756
Daniel Smith, Jr.	1756–1773
Robert Smith	1774–1815
Burr Woolman	1815–1844
Franklin Woolman	1844–1888
Henry S. Haines	1888–1922
Benjamin A. Sleeper	1922–1951
Henry J. Sherman	1951
Frank J. Sleeper	1953–1963
William H. Taylor	1963–

East New Jersey [2]

Robert Vauquillen	1674–?
Samuel Groom	1682–1683
William Haige	1683–1685
John Reid (acting)	1684
George Keith	1684–1716

(The conflict between Keith's authority from the governor, and Haige's authority from the Proprietors, was resolved 1685 in Keith's favor)

James Alexander	1715–1756
William Alexander	1756–1771
John Rutherfurd	1771–1804
Andrew Bell	1804–1842
S. V. R. Paterson	1842–1845
	1859–1866

East New Jersey [2] *(Cont.)*

Francis W. Brinley	1845–1859
Edward Brinley	1866–1867
John Rutherfurd	1867–1872
Monroe Howell	1872–1883
George H. Cook	1883–1889
John C. Goodridge, Jr.	1889–1901
Willis K. Howell	1901–1937
Lawrence B. Howell	1937–1949
Edward J. Grassmann	1949–1971
Edward J. Engel	1971–

Historical New Jersey Map Collections

American Geographical Society
Broadway at 156th Street, New York, N.Y. 10032

Camden County Historical Society
Park Blvd. and Euclid Ave., Camden, N.J. 08103

General Board of Proprietors of the Eastern Division of New Jersey
264 High Street, at Market St., Perth Amboy, N.J. 08861 (Visit by appt. only.)

The Joint Free Public Library of Morristown and Morris Township
Miller Rd. at South St., Morristown, N.J. 07960

Library of Congress, Geography & Map Division
845 S. Pickett St., Alexandria, Va.

Morristown National Historical Park, Washington Headquarters
Museum Library, Morris Ave. at Washington Ave., Morristown, N.J. 07960

Newark Public Library, New Jersey Division
Washington St. near Broad St., Newark, N.J. 07102

New Jersey Historical Society Library
230 Broadway, Newark, N.J. 07104

New Jersey State Library, Bureau of Archives and History
W. State St. near State House, Trenton, N.J. 08625

New-York Historical Society, Map and Print Room
170 Central Park West, at 77th St., New York, N.Y. 10024

New York Public Library, Map Division
Fifth Avenue at 42nd St., New York, N.Y. 10018

Princeton University Library, Map Room, also Rare Books Div.
Washington Rd. at William St., Princeton, N.J. 08540

Rutgers University Library, Special Collections
College Ave. near Huntington St., New Brunswick, N.J. 08903

West Jersey Proprietors
Broad St., between High & Wood Sts., Burlington, N.J. 08016 (Visit by appt. only.)

William L. Clements Library
University of Michigan, Ann Arbor, Michigan 48104

Notes

INTRODUCTION

1. Kemble Widmer, *The Geology and Geography of New Jersey* (Princeton: D. Van Nostrand Co., 1964), p. 9.

CHAPTER 1

1. R. V. Tooley, *Maps and Map-Makers* (New York: Bonanza Books, 1952), p. 29. Hereafter cited as Tooley, *Maps*.

2. Charles Bricker, *Landmarks of Mapmaking: An Illustrated Survey of Maps and Mapmakers* (Amsterdam: Elsevier, 1968), pp. 198–99, hereafter cited as Bricker, *Landmarks;* Emerson D. Fite and Archibald Freeman, *A Book of Old Maps, Delineating American History from the Earliest Days Down to the Close of the Revolutionary War* (Cambridge: Harvard University Press, 1926), pp. 10–12. Hereafter cited as Fite and Freeman, *Old Maps*.

3. *Ibid.,* pp. 24–27.

4. *Ibid.,* pp. 46–63.

5. I. N. Phelps Stokes, *The Iconography of Manhattan Island, 1498–1909* (New York: Robert H. Dodd, 1915), Vol. II, p. 51. Hereafter cited as Stokes, *Iconography.*

6. *Ibid.,* Vol. II, p. 70.

7. *Ibid.,* Vol. II, p. 86.

8. Lloyd A. Brown, *The Story of Maps* (New York: Little, Brown & Co., 1949), p. 168, hereafter cited as Brown, *Story of Maps.* Tooley, *Maps,* p. 33.

9. Robert M. Lunny, *Early Maps of North America* (Newark: *New Jersey Historical Society,* 1961), p. 20. Hereafter cited as Lunny, *Early Maps.*

10. Adrian C. Leiby, *The Early Dutch and Swedish Settlers of New Jersey* (Princeton: D. Van Nostrand Co., 1964), p. 17.

11. William A. Whitehead, *et al.,* eds., *Documents Relating to the Colonial History of the State of New Jersey, Archives of the State of N.J.* (Newark: Daily Journal Establishment, 1880 *et seq.*), Vol. 18 (1st series), pp. 15–17. Hereafter cited as Whitehead, *Documents.*

12. James, Duke of York, Indenture of June 23, 1664 (West Jersey Proprietors Office, Burlington, N.J.).

13. New York-New Jersey Boundary Dispute, July 18, 1769.

14. Whitehead, *Documents,* Vol. 18 (1st series), pp. 15–17.

15. Harold J. Barker, Jr., *Mapping Digest for New Jersey* (Trenton: Department of Conservation and Economic Development, Bureau of Geology and Topography, 1965), Bulletin 66, p. 1. Hereafter cited as Barker, *Mapping Digest.*

16. Rutgers University Library, Special Collections.

17. John P. Snyder, *The Story of New Jersey's Civil Boundaries, 1606–1968* (Trenton: Bureau of Geology and Topography, 1969), p. 51. Hereafter cited as Snyder, *Civil Boundaries.*

18. Stokes, *Iconography,* Vol. I, pp. 143–49.

19. *Ibid.*

20. Rutgers University Library, Special Collections.

21. Stokes, *Iconography,* Vol. I, p. 222.

22. Capt. Richard C. Holcomb, "The Early Dutch Maps of Upper Delaware Valley," *Proceedings of the New Jersey Historical Society,* New Series, Vol. 11, 1926, pp. 20–21. Hereafter cited as Holcomb, *Early Dutch Maps.*

23. Lunny, *Early Maps,* p. 23; Tooley, *Maps,* p. 52.

24. Stokes, *Iconography,* Vol. I, p. 213.

25. Fite and Freeman, *Old Maps,* pp. 150–52; *A Mapp of New Jersey in America by John Seller and William Fisher, London, 1677. A Note on the Facsimile issued by the John Carter Brown Library, Brown University* (Providence, R.I., 1958).

26. Holcomb, *Early Dutch Maps,* pp. 43–45.

27. Gabriel Thomas, *An Historical and Geographical Account of the Province and Country of Pensilvania; and of West-New-Jersey in America . . . with a Map of both Countries* (London: A Baldwin, 1698).

28. Library of Congress, Geography and Map Division.

29. General Board of Proprietors of the Eastern Division of New Jersey.

30. The Rev. W. Northey Jones, M.A., *The History of St. Peter's Church in Perth Amboy, N.J.* (Perth Amboy, 1924), pp. 28, 29. Hereafter cited as Jones, *St. Peter's Church.*

31. John E. Pomfret, *The Province of West New Jersey, 1609–1702* (Princeton: Princeton University Press, 1956), pp. 242–44. Hereafter cited as Pomfret, *West New Jersey.*

32. Jones, *St. Peter's Church,* pp. 28–29.

33. Pomfret, *West New Jersey,* p. 249.

34. *Ibid.,* p. 258.

35. Richard P. McCormick, *New Jersey from Colony to State, 1609–1789* (Princeton: D. Van Nostrand Co., 1964; New Brunswick: Rutgers University Press, 1972), p. 52, hereafter cited as McCormick, *New Jersey;* Elton D. Trueblood, *Robert Barclay* (New York: Harper & Row, 1968), p. 46.

36. Lunny, *Early Maps,* p. 23; Joseph S. Sickler, *The History of Salem County, New Jersey* (Salem: Sunbeam Publishing Co., 1937), p. 58.

37. *Proceedings of the New Jersey Historical Society,* New Series, Vol. 9, 1924, pp. 312–14; Pomfret, *New Jersey Proprietors and their Lands, 1664–1776* (Prince-

ton: D. Van Nostrand Co., 1964), pp. 94–110; Whitehead, *Documents,* Vol. 4 (1st series), pp. 399–401.

38. Julian P. Boyd, *Fundamental Laws and Constitutions of New Jersey* (Princeton: D. Van Nostrand Co., 1964), pp. 79–80.

39. General Board of Proprietors of the Eastern Division of New Jersey, Surveys, Vol. S1 (1716–1743/4). Manuscript volume at Perth Amboy headquarters.

40. *West Jersey Proprietors,* Burlington, N.J.: N.P., 1964.

41. George J. Miller, Registrar, General Board of Proprietors of the Eastern Division of New Jersey, personal communication, 1971.

42. Christopher Colles, *A Survey of the Roads of the United States of America, 1789,* ed. Walter W. Ristow (Cambridge: Belknap Press of Harvard University Press, 1961), p. 96. Hereafter cited as Colles, *Survey.*

43. Wheaton J. Lane, *From Indian Trail to Iron Horse, 1620–1860* (Princeton: Princeton University Press, 1939), p. 48. Hereafter cited as Lane, *Indian Trail.*

44. McCormick, *New Jersey,* pp. 55–57.

45. John Reading, Jr., "Journal of John Reading," 1715, 1716, 1719, *Proceedings of the New Jersey Historical Society,* 3rd series, Vol. 10 (1915), pp. 35–46, 90–110, 128–133.

46. Whitehead, *Documents,* Vol. 10 (1st series), p. 302.

47. W. Woodford Clayton, compiler, *History of Union and Middlesex Counties, N.J.* (Philadelphia: Everts and Peck, 1882), pp. 441–42.

48. New-York Historical Society; Rutgers University Library, Special Collections.

49. New-York Historical Society.

50. *Ibid.*

51. Walter Klinefelter, "Lewis Evans and His Maps," *Transactions of the American Philosophical Society,* New Series, Vol. 61, Part 7 (1971), p. 17, hereafter cited as Klinefelter, *Lewis Evans . . . ;* George J. Miller, *The Printing of the Elizabethtown Bill in Chancery* (Perth Amboy: privately printed, 1942).

52. James Parker, printer, *A Bill in the Chancery of New-Jersey, at the Suit of John Earl of Stair, and others, Proprietors of the Eastern-Division of New-Jersey; against Benjamin Bond, and some other Persons of Elizabeth-Town, distinguished by the Name of the Clinker Lot Right Men . . .* (New York, 1747).

53. Rutgers University Library, Special Collections.

54. Lawrence Henry Gipson, *Lewis Evans* (Philadelphia: The Historical Society of Pennsylvania, 1939), pp. 5–14, 75–77. Hereafter cited as Gipson, *Lewis Evans.*

55. T[homas] Pownall (ed. Lois Mulkearn from 1784 ms.), *A Topographical Description of the Dominions of the United States of America* (Pittsburgh: University of Pittsburgh Press, 1949), pp. 115, 152. Hereafter cited as Pownall, *Topographical.*

56. Gipson, *Lewis Evans,* pp. 21–23; Klinefelter, *Lewis Evans . . . ,* p. 22.

57. Pownall, *Topographical,* p. 14.

58. *Ibid.,* p. 16.

59. Klinefelter, *Lewis Evans . . . ,* pp. 54–56.

60. Pownall, *Topographical,* pp. 10–11.

61. Klinefelter, *Lewis Evans . . . ,* pp. 54–56.

62. Barker, *Mapping Digest,* p. 10.

63. Whitehead, *Documents,* Vol. 6 (1st series), pp. 154–62.

64. Snyder, *Civil Boundaries,* pp. 8, 36, 37.

65. *Ibid.,* p. 14.

CHAPTER 2

1. Fite and Freeman, *Old Maps,* p. 181.

2. Franklin K. Van Zandt, *Boundaries of the United States and the Several States,* Geological Survey Bulletin 1212 (Washington: U.S. Government Printing Office, 1966), p. 32.

3. Rutgers University Library, Special Collections.

4. Bricker, *Landmarks,* p. 224.

5. Pownall, *Topographical,* p. 8.

6. Rutgers University Library, Special Collections.

7. Pownall, *Topographical,* pp. 7, 8.

8. New-York Historical Society.

9. [Howard C. Rice, Jr.], *New Jersey Road Maps of the 18th Century* (Princeton: Princeton University Library, 1964). Hereafter cited as Rice, *Road Maps.*

10. Snyder, *Civil Boundaries,* p. 32.

11. Charles H. Winfield, *History of the Land Titles in Hudson County, N.J.* (New York: Wynkoop & Hallenbeck, 1872), pp. 30–32. Hereafter cited as Winfield, *Hudson County.*

12. Snyder, *Civil Boundaries,* p. 34.

13. New-York Historical Society.

14. *Ibid.*

15. Winfield, *Hudson County,* pp. vii, viii, 29.

16. New Jersey State Library, Bureau of Archives and History.

17. New-York Historical Society.

18. *The Petitions and Memorials of the Proprietors of East and West-Jersey to the Legislature of New-Jersey* (New York: Shepard Kollock, 1784).

19. Tooley, *Maps,* p. 56.

20. Library of Congress, Geography and Map Division.

21. Barker, *Mapping Digest,* p. 1.

22. *Newark Sunday Call,* September 4, 1932.

23. New Jersey Historical Society; Princeton University Library.

24. New-York Historical Society.

25. Albert H. Heusser, ed. Hubert G. Schmidt, *George Washington's Map-Maker: A Biography of Robert Erskine* (New Brunswick: Rutgers University Press, 1966). Hereafter cited as Heusser, *Washington's Map-Maker.*

26. *Ibid.,* p. 20.

27. *Ibid.,* p. 161.

28. *Ibid.,* pp. 163–65.

29. Peter J. Guthorn, *American Maps and Map Makers of the Revolution* (Monmouth Beach, N.J.: Philip Freneau Press, 1966), pp. 8, 26, 32.

30. *Ibid.,* p. 13.

31. Heusser, *Washington's Map-Maker,* pp. 209–11.

32. *Ibid.,* p. 209.

33. Colles, *Survey,* p. 64.

34. John T. Cunningham, *New Jersey: America's Main Road* (Garden City, N.Y.: Doubleday & Co. Inc., 1966), pp. 106–7. Hereafter cited as Cunningham, *New Jersey: America's Main Road.*

35. Rice, *Road Maps.*

36. Lane, *Indian Trail,* pp. 81, 86.

37. Colles, *Survey,* p. 97.

38. Lane, *Indian Trail,* pp. 125–26.

39. Colles, *Survey,* p. 20.

40. *Ibid.,* pp. 21–24.

41. *Ibid.,* pp. 44, 45.

42. *Ibid.,* pp. 53–58.

43. *Ibid.,* p .73.

44. Colles, *Survey.*

45. Dumas Malone and Allen Johnson, eds. *Dictionary of American Biography* (New York: Charles Scribner's Sons, 1943). Hereafter cited as Malone, *American Biography.*

46. Harold J. Barker, Jr., personal communication, 1971.

47. General Board of Proprietors of the Eastern Division of New Jersey.

48. Camden County Historical Society; Library of Congress, Geography and Map Division.

49. Rutgers University Library, Special Collections; Malone, *American Biography.*

50. Rutgers University Library, Special Collections.

CHAPTER 3

1. Lane, *Indian Trail,* pp. 144–51.

2. *Newark Star,* Feb. 15, 1939.

3. Lane, *Indian Trail,* p. 226.

4. New Jersey Geological Survey, *Annual Report of the State Geologist for the Year 1885* (Trenton: John L. Murphy Pub. Co.), p. 208. Hereafter cited as *Annual Report of the State Geologist, 1885.*

5. Colles, *Survey,* p. 102.

6. Rice, *Road Maps.*

7. Rutgers University Library, Special Collections.

8. *Acts of the Legislature of the State of New Jersey,* P.L. 1799, p. 652. Hereafter cited as *Acts of the Legislature.*

9. *Ibid.,* P.L. 1822, p. 98.

10. Rutgers University Library, Special Collections.

11. *Annual Report of the State Geologist,* 1885, p. 187.

12. *Acts of the Legislature,* P.L. 1828, p. 218; P.L. 1831, p. 113; P.L. 1847, p. 190.

13. William Nelson, "Fifty Years of Historical Work in New Jersey," *Proceedings of the New Jersey Historical Society,* 2nd series, Vol. 13, 1894–95, pp. 251–52; Hamilton Schuyler, *A History of St. Michael's Church, Trenton . . . 1703 to 1926* (Princeton: Princeton University Press, 1926), p. 207.

14. Thomas [F.] Gordon, *Gazetteer of the State of New Jersey* (Trenton: Daniel Fenton, 1834), p. 162.

15. *New Jersey State Gazette,* May 31, 1834. Typed copy, E. T. Hutchinson papers, Rutgers University Library, Special Collections.

16. The Rev. S. F. Hotchkin, Doylestown (Pa.). *Daily Democrat,* June 10, 1907.

17. Rutgers University Library, Special Collections.

18. Bricker, *Landmarks,* p. 35.

19. A. Joseph Wraight and Elliott B. Roberts, *The Coast and Geodetic Survey, 1807–1957: 150 Years of History* (Washington: U.S. Department of Commerce, Coast and Geodetic Survey: U.S. Government Printing Office, 1957).

20. *Annual Report of the State Geologist,* 1885, p. 156.

21. *Acts of the Legislature,* P.L. 1854, p. 176.

22. *Annual Report of the State Geologist,* 1885, pp. 162, 165.

23. *Acts of the Legislature,* P.L. 1860, p. 280.

24. Rutgers University Library, Special Collections.

25. *Acts of the Legislature,* P.L. 1863, p. 87; *Annual Report of the State Geologist,* 1885, pp. 162, 165.

26. New Jersey Historical Society.

27. Rutgers University Library, Special Collections.

28. *Ibid.*

29. Richard W. Stephenson, *Land Ownership Maps* (Washington: Library of Congress, 1967), p. xiv. Hereafter cited as Stephenson, *Land Ownership Maps.*

30. Agnes B. Grametbaur, "Annotated Bibliography and Index of Atlases and Maps of New Jersey, 1800 to 1949" (typescript, Rutgers University Library, Special Collections; Newark Public Library; New York Public Library). Hereafter cited as Grametbaur, "Annotated Bibliography."

31. Carl Raymond Woodward and Ingrid Nelson Waller, *New Jersey's Agricultural Experiment Station, 1880–1930* (New Brunswick: Agricultural Experiment Station, 1932), pp. 15–22.

32. *New Jersey Equity Reports,* Vol. 72 (1909), pp. 56–131.

33. *Annual Report of the State Geologist, 1885,* p. 170.

34. New Jersey Historical Society.

35. New Jersey Geological Survey, *Final Report of the State Geologist,* Vol. I (Trenton: John L. Murphy Pub. Co., 1888), pp. 2–3. Hereafter cited as *Final Report of the State Geologist,* 1888.

36. *Annual Report of the State Geologist,* 1885, p. 189.

37. *Final Report of the State Geologist,* 1888, pp. 2–3.

38. *Ibid.,* p. 7.

39. Francis Bazley Lee, *History of New Jersey* (Newark: Newark Book Publishing and Engraving Co., 1905), p. 180.

40. *New York Times,* Feb. 2, 1950; J. J. Scannell, ed. and pub., *New Jersey's First Citizens and State Guide* (Paterson, N.J., 1919), pp. 465–67.

41. Mrs. C. C. Vermeule, Jr., personal communication, 1971.

42. *Final Report of the State Geologist,* 1888, p. 10.

43. *Annual Report of the State Geologist,* 1885, p. 9.

44. *Final Report of the State Geologist,* 1888, p. 15.

45. *Annual Report of the State Geologist,* 1885, pp. 196–97.

46. *Ibid.,* p. 14.

47. *Final Report of the State Geologist,* 1888, pp. 231–75.

48. Barker, *Mapping Digest,* p. 2.

49. Barker, personal communication, 1972.

50. Newark Public Library; Princeton University Library; Rutgers University Library, Special Collections; others.

CHAPTER 4

1. Rutgers University Library, Special Collections.

2. Hubert R. Cornish, *New Jersey: A Story of Progress* (New York: Charles Scribner's Sons, 1931), pp. 157, 159; J. Joseph Gribbins, ed. and pub., *Manual of the Legislature of New Jersey* (Trenton, 1972), p. 156.

3. *Acts of the Legislature,* P.L. 1912, p. 828; P.L. 1917, p. 25.

4. *Newark Ledger,* Jan. 5, 1947.

5. *New York Times,* Dec. 28, 1952.

6. Brown, *Story of Maps,* p. 278.

7. Barker, *Mapping Digest,* pp. 3–4.

8. William B. Matthews, Jr., *The Macmillan Marine Atlas, New Jersey and Delaware Waters* (New York: The Macmillan Co., 1968).

9. U.S. Department of Commerce, Coast and Geodetic Survey, *Plane Coordinate Intersection Tables (2½-Minute), New Jersey.* Special Publication No. 333 (Washington: U.S. Government Printing Office, 1955).

10. U.S. Department of Commerce, Coast and Geodetic Survey, *Plane-Coordinate Systems,* Serial No. 562 (Washington: U.S. Government Printing Office, 1948).

11. Barker, *Mapping Digest,* pp. 7, 9.

12. Brown, *Story of Maps,* p. 276; Charles H. Deetz and Oscar S. Adams, *Elements of Map Projection.* U.S. Department of Commerce, Coast and Geodetic Survey. Special Publication No. 68, 4th ed. (Washington: U.S. Government Printing Office, 1934), p. 58.

13. *Ibid.,* p. 77; Paul D. Thomas, *Conformal Projections in Geodesy and Cartography.* U.S. Department of Commerce, Coast and Geodetic Survey. Special Publication No. 251 (Washington: U.S. Government Printing Office, 1952), pp. 90–91.

14. Barker, personal communication, 1972.

15. Barker, *Mapping Digest,* p. 10.

16. *The Evening News* (Newark, N.J.), April 16, 1971.

17. David Greenhood, *Mapping* (Chicago: University of Chicago Press, 1964), pp. 104–10.

18. *The Evening News* (Newark, N.J.), March 24, 1971; *Plain Facts about New Jersey's Environment: The Wetlands.* New Jersey Department of Environmental Protection (1971).

19. General Drafting Co., Inc., *Of Maps and Mapping* (Convent Station, N.J., 1959). Hereafter cited as General Drafting, *Of Maps and Mapping.*

20. Arthur W. Baum, "Map Maker for Millions," *Saturday Evening Post,* May 14, 1960, p. 48 (Philadelphia: Curtis Publishing Co., 1960); Herbert Dalmar, "He Has It All Mapped Out," *Reader's Digest,* November, 1954. Condensed from *Travel;* Otto G. Lindberg, *My Story* (Convent Station, N.J.: General Drafting Co., Inc., 1955).

21. *Oilways,* No. 2 (Houston, Texas: Marketing Department, Humble Oil & Refining Co., 1969), pp. 15–16.

22. General Drafting, *Of Maps and Mapping,* pp. 22–23.

23. Arthur W. Baum, "Map Maker for Millions," *Saturday Evening Post,* May 14, 1960.

24. Arden Davis Melick, "Maplewood's Map Maker," *Suburban Life,* February 1967, pp. 38–39; Kate Wilson, personal communications, 1970–71.

25. *Ibid.*

26. David B. Carlisle, "World's Their Worry," Passaic *Herald-News,* July 23, 1969.

27. Rutgers University Library, Special Collections.

28. Cunningham, *New Jersey: America's Main Road,* pp. 240–41.

29. Rutgers University Library, Special Collections.

30. *Ibid.*

31. *Acts of the Legislature,* P.L. 1917, p. 25.

32. Grametbaur, "Annotated Bibliography."

33. *Ibid.*

34. Barker, *Mapping Digest,* pp. 49–64.

35. Snyder, *Civil Boundaries.*

36. *New York Walk Book,* 4th ed. New York-New Jersey Trail Conference & the American Geographical Society (Garden City: Doubleday, 1971).

APPENDIX A

1. Grametbaur, "Annotated Bibliography"; Stephenson, *Land Ownership Maps,* pp. 24–26.

2. New-York Historical Society.

APPENDIX C

1. Barker, personal communication, 1971.

2. Grametbaur, "Annotated Bibliography."

Appendix D

1. Based on Grametbaur, "Annotated Bibliography," and collections at Rutgers University Library, Special Collections; The Joint Free Public Library of Morristown and Morris Township.

Appendix E

1. Barker, personal communication, 1971; updated, 1972.

Appendix F

1. *West Jersey Proprietors.*
2. Miller, personal communication, 1971.

Bibliography

Books and Articles, General

Barker, Harold J., Jr. *Mapping Digest for New Jersey*. Trenton: Dept. of Conservation and Economic Development, Bureau of Geology and Topography, 1965. Bulletin 66.

Bricker, Charles. *Landmarks of Mapmaking, An Illustrated Survey of Maps and Mapmakers*. Amsterdam: Elsevier, 1968.

Brown, Lloyd A. *The Story of Maps*. New York: Bonanza Books, reprint of 1949 edition of Little, Brown & Co.

Clayton, W. Woodford, compiler. *History of Union and Middlesex Counties, N.J.* Philadelphia: Everts and Peck, 1882.

Cornish, Hubert R. *New Jersey, A Story of Progress*. New York: Charles Scribner's Sons, 1931.

Cunningham, John T. *New Jersey, America's Main Road*. Garden City, N.Y.: Doubleday & Co., Inc., 1966.

Fisher, E. J. *New Jersey as a Royal Province 1738–1776*. New York: Columbia Univ., 1911.

Gribbins, J. Joseph, editor and pub. *Manual of the Legislature of New Jersey*. Trenton, 1972. (Pub. annually.)

Hood, John. *Index of Colonial and State Laws of New Jersey, 1663–1903*. Camden, N.J.: Sinnickson Chew & Sons Co., 1905.

Justice, Joseph, printer. *Laws of the State of New Jersey*. 1821. (Compilations from about 1710 to 1821.)

Kennedy, S. M., executive editor. *The New Jersey Almanac*. Upper Montclair, N.J.: The N.J. Almanac, Inc., 1963.

Lane, Wheaton J. *From Indian Trail to Iron Horse, 1620–1860*. Princeton, N.J.: Princeton Univ. Press, 1939.

Lee, Francis Bazley. *History of New Jersey*. Newark: Newark Book Publishing and Engraving Co., 1905.

————. *New Jersey as a Colony and as a State*. New York: The Publishing Society of N.J., 1903.

New Jersey Department of Transportation. *Local Names and Municipalities*. Trenton: n.d.

New Jersey History Committee. *Outline History of New Jersey.* New Brunswick, N.J.: Rutgers Univ. Press, 1950.

New York-New Jersey Trail Conference & the American Geographical Society. *New York Walk Book.* 4th ed. Garden City, N.Y.: Doubleday, 1971.

Snyder, John P. *The Story of New Jersey's Civil Boundaries, 1606–1968.* Trenton: Bureau of Geology and Topography, 1969.

Tanner, Edwin P. *The Province of New Jersey 1664–1738.* New York: Columbia Univ., 1908.

U.S. Department of the Interior. *Boundaries of the United States and the Several States,* by Franklin K. Van Zandt. Geological Survey Bulletin 1212, 1966. Washington: U.S. Government Printing Office.

Wacker, Peter O. *The Musconetcong Valley of New Jersey—A Historical Geography.* New Brunswick: Rutgers Univ. Press, 1968.

West Jersey Proprietors. Booklet issued 1964. Burlington, N.J.

Widmer, Kemble. *The Geology and Geography of New Jersey.* Princeton: D. Van Nostrand Co., 1964.

Books and Articles: Mapping Before 1800

Boyd, Julian P. *Fundamental Laws and Constitutions of New Jersey.* Princeton: D. Van Nostrand Co., Inc., 1964.

Brown, Elizabeth Stow. "An Examination of Old Maps of Northern New Jersey." *Proceedings of the New Jersey Historical Society,* 3rd series, Vol. 4, 1902, pp. 65–74.

Colles, Christopher. *A Survey of the Roads of the United States of America, 1789.* Cambridge, Mass.: Belknap Press of Harvard Univ. Press, 1961. Edited by Walter W. Ristow.

Fite, Emerson D. and Archibald Freeman. *A Book of Old Maps Delineating American History from the Earliest Days Down to the Close of the Revolutionary War.* Cambridge: Harvard University Press, 1926. (Reprinted 1969 by Dover Publications, Inc.)

General Board of Proprietors of the Eastern Division of New Jersey. Surveys, Vol. S.1 (1716–1743/4). Manuscript volume held at Perth Amboy headquarters.

Gipson, Lawrence Henry. *Lewis Evans.* Philadelphia: The Historical Society of Pennsylvania, 1939.

Guthorn, Peter J. *American Maps and Map Makers of the Revolution.* Monmouth Beach, N.J.: Philip Freneau Press, 1966.

————. *British Maps of the American Revolution.* Monmouth Beach, N.J.: Philip Freneau Press, 1972.

————. "The Role of New Jersey in British Strategy, as Demonstrated by Maps." Fourth Annual New Jersey History Symposium, sponsored by New Jersey Historical Commission. Trenton, N.J., Dec. 2, 1972. To be published 1973.

————. "Some Notable New Jersey Maps of the Dutch Colonial Period." *Proceedings of the New Jersey Historical Society,* Vol. 80, 1962. pp. 102–110.

Heusser, Albert H. *George Washington's Map Maker, A Biography of Robert Erskine.* New Brunswick: Rutgers Univ. Press. Edited with an introduction by

Hubert G. Schmidt. (Originally published 1928, titled *The Forgotten General, Robert Erskine.*) 1966.

Holcomb, Capt. Richmond C. "The Early Dutch Maps of Upper Delaware Valley." *Proceedings of the New Jersey Historical Society,* New Series, Vol. 11, 1926. pp. 18–45.

Klinefelter, Walter. "Lewis Evans and His Maps." *Transactions of the American Philosophical Society,* New Series, Vol. 61, Part 7, 1971.

Leaming, Aaron, and Jacob Spicer. *The Grants, Concessions and Original Constitutions of the Province of New-Jersey.* Philadelphia: W. Bradford, 1758.

Leiby, Adrian C. *The Early Dutch and Swedish Settlers of New Jersey.* Princeton: D. Van Nostrand Co., 1964.

Lunny, Robert M. *Early Maps of North America.* Newark: The New Jersey Historical Society, 1961.

A Mapp of New Jersey in America by John Seller and William Fisher, London, 1677. A Note on the Facsimile issued by the John Carter Brown Library, Brown University. Providence, Rhode Island, 1958.

McCormick, Richard P. *New Jersey from Colony to State—1609–1789.* Princeton: D. Van Nostrand Co., 1964; New Brunswick: Rutgers University Press, 1972.

Miller, George J. *The Printing of the Elizabethtown Bill in Chancery.* Perth Amboy. Privately printed, 1942.

New York-New Jersey Boundary Dispute: "To the Honourable His Majesty's Commissioners for settling the Partition-Line, between the Colonies of New-York and New-Jersey" ("the Demands . . . of New-York, against . . . New-Jersey"), July 18, 1769.

Parker, James, printer. *A Bill in the Chancery of New-Jersey, at the Suit of John Earl of Stair, and others, Proprietors of the Eastern-Division of New-Jersey; against Benjamin Bond, and some other Persons of Elizabeth-Town, distinguished by the Name of the Clinker Lot Right Men . . . .* New-York. 1747.

Paterson, William, compiler. *Laws of the State of New Jersey.* Newark: Matthias Day, 1800. (Quotes many of the laws of 1703–1799.)

The Petitions and Memorials of the Proprietors of East and West-Jersey to the Legislature of New Jersey. New York: Shepard Kollock, 1784.

Pomfret, John E. *The New Jersey Proprietors and Their Lands, 1664–1776.* Princeton: D. Van Nostrand Co., Inc., 1964.

————. *The Province of East New Jersey 1609–1702.* Princeton, N.J.: Princeton Univ. Press, 1962.

————. *The Province of West New Jersey 1609–1702.* Princeton, N.J.: Princeton Univ. Press, 1956.

Pownall, T(homas). *A Topographical Description of the Dominions of the United States of America.* Pittsburgh: Univ. of Pittsburgh Press, 1949. Edited by Lois Mulkearn from a 1784 manuscript.

Reading, John, Jr., "Journal of John Reading." Written 1715, 1716, 1719, published in *Proceedings of the New Jersey Historical Society,* 3rd series, Vol. 10, 1915. pp. 35–46, 90–110, 128–133.

Reed, H. Clay, and Geo. J. Miller. *The Burlington Court Book*. Washington, D.C.: American Historical Assn., 1944.

[Rice, Howard C. Jr., ed.] *New Jersey Road Maps of the 18th Century*. Princeton: Princeton University Library, 1964.

Rice, Howard C., Jr. and Anne S. K. Brown, translators and editors. *The American Campaigns of Rochambeau's Army, 1780–1783*. Princeton, N.J. and Providence, R.I.: Princeton University Press and Brown University Press, 1972.

Sickler, Joseph S. *The History of Salem County New Jersey*. Salem: Sunbeam Publishing Co., 1937.

Stokes, I. N. Phelps. *The Iconography of Manhattan Island, 1498–1909*. New York: Robert H. Dodd, 1915. Volumes I and II.

Thomas, Gabriel. *An Historical and Geographical Account of the Province and Country of Pensilvania; and of West-New-Jersey in America . . . with a Map of both Countries*. London: A. Baldwin, 1698.

Tooley, R. V. *Maps and Map-Makers*. New York: Bonanza Books, 1952. Reprint of 1952 edition by B. T. Batsford Ltd., pub.

Vermeule, Cornelius C. "Early Transportation In and About New Jersey." *Proceedings of the New Jersey Historical Society*, 3rd series, Vol. 9, 1924. pp. 106–124.

Whitehead, William, *et al.*, editors. *Documents Relating to the Colonial History of the State of New Jersey, Archives of the State of N.J.* Newark: Daily Journal Establishment, 1880 et seq.

Whitehead, William A. "The Northern Boundary Line." *Proceedings of the New Jersey Historical Society*, 1859. pp. 157–186.

Winfield, Charles H. *History of the Land Titles in Hudson County, N.J.* New York: Wynkoop & Hallenbeck, 1872.

Books and Articles: Mapping Since 1800

Baum, Arthur W. "Map Maker for Millions." *Saturday Evening Post*. Philadelphia: Curtis Publishing Co. p. 48. May 14, 1960.

Bloomfield, Joseph, compiler. *Laws of the State of New Jersey*. Trenton: J. J. Wilson, 1811. (Quotes many of the laws of 1800–1811.)

Carlisle, David B. "World's Their Worry." *The Herald-News*. Passaic, N.J. July 23, 1969.

Cunningham, John T. "Around New Jersey via the Armchair Route." *Newark Sunday News* magazine. Newark, N.J. Dec. 11, 1960.

Dalmas, Herbert. "He Has It All Mapped Out." *Reader's Digest*. Pleasantville, N.Y. Nov. 1954. Condensed from *Travel*.

Effross, Harris I. "Origins of Post-Colonial Counties in N.J." *Proceedings of the New Jersey Historical Society*, New series, Vol. 81, 1963. pp. 103–122.

General Drafting Co., Inc. *Of Maps and Mapping*. Convent Station, N.J., 1959.

Gordon, Thomas [F.] *Gazetteer of the State of New Jersey*. Trenton: Daniel Fenton, 1834.

Grametbaur, Agnes B. "Annotated Bibliography and Index of Atlases and Maps of New Jersey, 1800 to 1949." Original of typescript at Rutgers Univ. Library, Special Collections. Copies at Newark and New York Public Libraries. Prepared on grant while author was administrative assistant of Dept. of Geology at Rutgers Univ. (1947–49). 1540 pp. Unpublished.

Greenhood, David. *Mapping*. Chicago: The University of Chicago Press, 1964.

Lindberg, Otto G. *My Story*. Convent Station, N.J.: General Drafting Co., Inc., 1955.

Matthews, William B., Jr. *The Macmillan Marine Atlas, New Jersey and Delaware Waters*. New York: The Macmillan Co., 1968.

Melick, Arden Davis. "Maplewood's Map Maker." *Suburban Life*. Orange, N.J., Feb. 1967. pp. 38–9.

Neilson, James. "Dr. George H. Cook." *Proceedings of the New Jersey Historical Society*, 2nd series, Vol. 11, 1890. pp. 53–63.

Nelson, William. "Fifty Years of Historical Work in New Jersey." *Proceedings of the New Jersey Historical Society*, 2nd series, Vol. 13, 1894–95.

New Jersey Boundary Commission. *Reports and Proceedings, 1890.*

New Jersey Department of Environmental Protection. *Plain Facts about New Jersey's Environment—The Wetlands*, 1971.

New Jersey Geological Survey. *Annual Report of the State Geologist for the Year 1885*. Trenton: John L. Murphy Pub. Co.

————. *Final Report of the State Geologist, Vol. I*. Trenton: John L. Murphy Pub. Co., 1888.

Stephenson, Richard W. *Land Ownership Maps*. Washington: Library of Congress, 1967.

U.S. Department of Commerce. Coast and Geodetic Survey. *Elements of Map Projection*, by Charles H. Deetz and Oscar S. Adams. Special Publication No. 68, 4th ed., 1934. Washington: U.S. Government Printing Office.

————. ————. *Conformal Projections in Geodesy and Cartography*, by Paul D. Thomas. Special Publication No. 251, 1952. Washington: U.S. Government Printing Office.

————. ————. *Plane Coordinate Intersection Tables (2½-Minute), New Jersey*. Special Publication No. 333, 1955. Washington: U.S. Government Printing Office.

————. ————. *Plane-Coordinate Systems*. Serial No. 562, 1948. Washington: U.S. Government Printing Office.

————. ————. *The Coast and Geodetic Survey 1807–1957, 150 Years of History*, by A. Joseph Wraight and Elliott B. Roberts. Washington: U.S. Government Printing Office, 1957.

Woodward, Carl Raymond and Ingrid Nelson Waller. *New Jersey's Agricultural Experiment Station, 1880–1930*. New Brunswick, N.J.: Agricultural Experiment Station, 1932.

Index

Note: Reproduced maps are indexed by caption data only. Names in the Appendix are rarely indexed unless also occurring elsewhere in the text.

ABOUT THE AUTHOR

John P. Snyder has made a hobby of maps since childhood, and when he moved to New Jersey in 1953 this interest became closely related to New Jersey history.

Mr. Snyder received degrees in chemical engineering from Purdue University and Massachusetts Institute of Technology. A registered professional engineer in New Jersey and Ohio, he is presently senior project engineer at CIBA-GEIGY Corp. in Summit, New Jersey.

Mr. Snyder's first book, *The Story of New Jersey's Civil Boundaries, 1606–1968,* published in 1969, received the Award of Merit of the American Association for State and Local History. He is the author of several magazine articles on civil boundaries, map projections, and engineering.

The text of this book was set in Baskerville Linotype and printed by offset on Warren's #1854 manufactured by S. D. Warren Company, Boston, Mass. Composed, printed and bound by Quinn & Boden Company, Inc., Rahway, N.J.